RANCH
HOME PLANS

W9-DFF-547

Ranch Home Plans is a collection of our best-selling ranch homes in a variety of styles. These plans cover a wide range of architectural styles. A broad assortment is presented to match a wide variety of lifestyles and budgets. Each design page features floor plans, a front view of the house, interior square footage of the home, number of bedrooms, baths, garage size and foundation types. All floor plans show room and exterior dimensions.

Technical Specifications

At the time the construction drawings were prepared, every effort was made to ensure that these plans and specifications meet nationally recognized building codes (BOCA, Southern Building Code Congress and others). Because national building codes change or vary from area to area some drawing modifications and/or the assistance of a professional designer or architect may be necessary to comply with your local codes or to accommodate specific building site conditions. We advise you to consult with your local building official for information regarding codes governing your area.

Blueprint Ordering - Fast and Easy

Your ordering is made simple by following the instructions on page 7. See page 6 for more information on which types of blueprint packages are available and how many plan sets to order.

Your Home, Your Way

The blueprints you receive are a master plan for building your new home. They start you on your way to what may well be the most rewarding experience of your life.

COVER HOME The house shown on the front cover is plan #M01-007D-0010 and is featured on page 19. Photo courtesy of HDA, Inc., St. Louis, Missouri.

RANCH HOME PLANS is published by HDA, Inc., 944 Anglum Road, St. Louis, MO, 63042. All rights reserved. Reproduction in whole or in part without written permission of the publisher is prohibited. Printed in U.S.A. © 2007.

Artist drawings and photos shown in this publication may vary slightly from the actual working drawings. Some photos are shown in mirror reverse. Please refer to the floor plan for accurate layout.

CONTENTS

MENARDS®

Current printing   5   4   3   2

Let MENARDS Make Your Dream Home A Reality

"Thanks to MENARDS®, finding and building our Dream Home has never been easier."

Thinking about building your dream home? Or, perhaps you are interested in a vacation home or downsizing to a single story home? Choosing a home plan can be a daunting task.

This book of Ranch Home Plans has been designed to make the search simple and easy. Browse the pages of this book and look for the style that best suits your family and your needs. These plans have been chosen from top designers from across the country and can provide to you the perfect home that will truly be a place of refuge for your whole family for years to come.

This book is the perfect place to begin your search for the home of your dreams. You will find the expected beauty you want and the functional efficiency you need, all designed with unmatched quality.

Also, keep in mind, this book contains helpful articles for understanding what kind of plan package you may need as well as other helpful building aids to make the process even easier.

When you have made this decision visit your local MENARDS® store to place your order and partner with one of their friendly team members to walk you through the process.

MENARDS® is dedicated to assist you through the entire home decision process.

What's The Right Plan For You?

Choosing a home plan is an exciting but difficult task. Many factors play a role in what home plan is best for you and your family. To help you get started, we have pinpointed some of the major factors to consider when searching for your dream home. Take the time to evaluate your family's needs and you will have an easier time sorting through all of the home plans offered in this book.

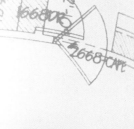

Budget: The first thing to consider is your budget. Many items take part in this budget, from ordering the blueprints to the last doorknob purchased. Once you have found your dream home plan, visit the **MENARDS**® Building Materials Desk to get a cost-to-build estimate to ensure that the finished product is still within your price range.

Family Lifestyle: After your budget is deciphered, you need to assess you and your family's lifestyle needs. Think about the stage of life you are at now, and what stages you will be going through in the future. Ask yourself questions to figure out how much room you need now and if you will need room for expansion. Are you married? Do you have children? How many children do you plan on having? Are you an empty-nester?

Incorporate in your planning any frequent guests you may have, including elderly parents, grandchildren or adult children who may live with you.

Does your family entertain a lot? If so, think about the rooms you will need to do so. Will you need both formal and informal spaces? Do you need a gourmet kitchen? Do you need a game room and/or a wet bar?

> Experts in the field suggest that the best way to determine your needs is to begin by listing everything you like or dislike about your current home.

Floor Plan Layouts: When looking through our home plans, imagine yourself walking through the house. Consider the flow from the entry to the living, sleeping and gathering areas. Does the layout ensure privacy for the master bedroom? Does the garage enter near the kitchen for easy unloading? Does the placement of the windows provide enough privacy from any neighboring properties? Do you plan on using furniture you already have? Will this furniture fit in the appropriate rooms? When you find a plan you want to purchase, be sure to picture yourself actually living in it.

Exterior Spaces: There are many different home styles ranging from Traditional to Contemporary. Flip through and find which style most appeals to you and the neighborhood in which you plan to build. Also think of your site and how the entire house will fit on this site. Picture any landscaping you plan on incorporating into the design. Using your imagination is key when choosing a home plan.

Choosing a home plan can be an intimidating experience. Asking yourself these questions before you get started on the search will help you through the process. With our large selection of multiple styles we are certain you will find your dream home in the following pages.

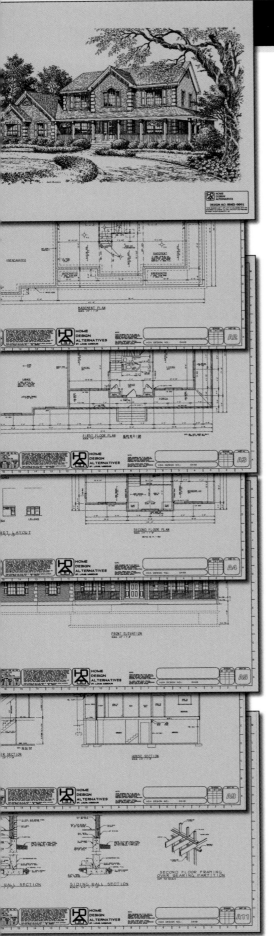

Our Blueprint Packages Offer...

Quality plans for building your future, with extras that provide unsurpassed value, ensure good construction and long-term enjoyment.

1. Cover Sheet

Included with many of the plans, the cover sheet is the artist's rendering of the exterior of the home. It will give you an idea of how your home will look when completed and landscaped.

2. Foundation

The foundation plan shows the layout of the basement, walk-out basement, crawl space, slab or pier foundation. All necessary notations and dimensions are included. See plan page for the foundation types included. If the home plan you choose does not have your desired foundation type, call or visit any **MENARDS**® and they can advise you on how to customize your foundation to suit your specific needs or site conditions.

3. Floor Plans

The floor plans show the placement of walls, doors, closets, plumbing fixtures, electrical outlets, columns, and beams for each level of the home.

4. Interior Elevations

Interior elevations provide views of special interior elements such as fireplaces, kitchen cabinets, built-in units and other features of the home.

5. Exterior Elevations

Exterior elevations illustrate the front, rear and both sides of the house, with all details of exterior materials and the required dimensions.

6. Sections

Show detail views of the home or portions of the home as if it were sliced from the roof to the foundation. This sheet shows important areas such as load-bearing walls, stairs, joists, trusses and other structural elements, which are critical for proper construction.

7. Details

Show how to construct certain components of your home, such as the roof system, stairs, deck, etc.

Your Blueprint Package will contain the necessary construction information to build your home. We also offer the following products and services to save you time and money in the building process.

Material List

Material lists are available for all the plans in this book. Each list gives you the quantity, dimensions and description of the building materials necessary to construct your home. You'll get faster and more accurate bids from your contractor while saving money by paying for only the materials you need. To receive a free home plan estimate call or visit any **MENARDS** Building Materials Desk.

Discount Price: $125.00 - Menards SKU 100-3422
Note: Material lists are not refundable.

Express Delivery

Most orders are processed within 24 hours of receipt. Please allow 7-10 business days for delivery. If you need to place a rush order, please call or visit any **MENARDS**® store to order by 11:00 a.m. Monday-Friday CST and specify you would like express service (allow 1-2 business days.

Discount Price: $40.00
Menards SKU 194-4356

Technical Assistance

If you have additional questions, call our technical support line at 1-314-770-2228 between 8:00 a.m. and 5:00 p.m. Monday-Friday CST. Whether it involves design modifications or field assistance, our designers are extremely familiar with all of our designs and will be happy to help you. We want your home to be everything you expect it to be.

Other Great Products . . .

The Legal Kit

Avoid many legal pitfalls and build your home with confidence using the forms and contracts featured in this kit. Included are request for proposal documents, various fixed price and cost plus contracts, instructions on how and when to use each form, warranty statements and more. Save time and money before you break ground on your new home or start a remodeling project. All forms are reproducible. The kit is ideal for homebuilders and contractors.

Discount Price: $35.00 - Menards SKU 100-3422

Detail Plan Packages -
Electrical, Plumbing & Framing Packages

Three separate packages offer homebuilders details for constructing various foundations; numerous floor, wall and roof framing techniques; simple to complex residential wiring; sump pump and water softener hookups; plumbing connection methods; installation of septic systems, and more. Each package includes three dimensional illustrations and a glossary of terms. Purchase one or all three. Note: These drawings do not pertain to a specific home plan.

Discount Price: $20.00 each or all three for $40.00
Menards SKU 100-3422

What Kind Of Plan Package Do You Need?

Now that you've found the home you've been looking for, here are some suggestions on how to make your Dream Home a reality. To get started, order the type of plans that fit your particular situation.

Your Choices

The One-Set Study Package*

We offer a One-set plan package so you can study your home in detail. This one set is considered a study set and is marked "not for construction." It is a copyright violation to reproduce blueprints.

The Minimum 5-Set Package*

If you're ready to start the construction process, this 5-Set package is the minimum number of blueprint sets you will need. It will require keeping close track of each set so they can be used by multiple subcontractors and tradespeople.

The Standard 8-Set Package*

For best results in terms of cost, schedule and quality of construction, we recommend you order eight (or more) sets of blueprints. Besides one set for yourself, additional sets of blueprints will be required by your mortgage lender, local building department, general contractor and all subcontractors working on foundation, electrical, plumbing, heating/air conditioning, carpentry work, etc.

Reproducible Masters

If you wish to make some minor design changes, you'll want to order reproducible masters. These drawings contain the same information as the blueprints but are printed on reproducible paper that is easy to alter and clearly indicates your right to copy or reproduce. This will allow your builder or a local design professional to make the necessary drawing changes without the major expense of redrawing the plans. This package also allows you to print copies of the modified plans as needed. The right of building only one structure from these plans is licensed exclusively to the buyer. You may not use this design to build a second or multiple dwelling(s) without purchasing another blueprint. Each violation of the Copyright Law is punishable in a fine.

Mirror Reverse Sets

Plans can be printed in mirror reverse. These plans are useful when the house would fit your site better if all the rooms were on the opposite side than shown. They are simply a mirror image of the original drawings causing the lettering and dimensions to read backwards. Therefore, when ordering mirror reverse drawings, you must purchase at least one set of right-reading plans.

*Additional sets of the same plan ordered are available only within 90 days after purchase of original plan package.

Discount Price: $45.00 - Menards SKU 194-4330

How To Order Home Plans

You've found your Dream Home, now what?

Follow these simple steps

1. Review the article on page 6 to decide what type of plan package you need.

2. To order, call or visit any **MENARDS** store and go to the Building Materials Desk.

To locate the **MENARDS** store nearest you go to **www.Menards.com**, click on Store Service then click on the Store locator.

Artist drawings and photos shown in this publication may vary slightly from the actual working drawings. Some photos are shown in mirror reverse. Please refer to the floor plan for accurate layout.

BLUEPRINT SKU PRICING

PRICE CODE		1-SET STUDY	5-SET PLAN	8-SET PLAN	REPRO. MASTERS
AAA	Menards SKU Discount Price	194-3920 $310	194-3933 $380	194-3946 $425	194-3959 $525
AA	Menards SKU Discount Price	194-3962 $410	194-3975 $480	194-3988 $525	194-3991 $625
A	Menards SKU Discount Price	194-4000 $470	194-4084 $540	194-4165 $585	194-4246 $686
B	Menards SKU Discount Price	194-4013 $530	194-4097 $600	194-4178 $645	194-4259 $745
C	Menards SKU Discount Price	194-4026 $585	194-4107 $655	194-4181 $700	194-4262 $800
D	Menards SKU Discount Price	194-4039 $635	194-4110 $705	194-4194 $750	194-4275 $850
E	Menards SKU Discount Price	194-4042 $695	194-4123 $765	194-4204 $810	194-4288 $910
F	Menards SKU Discount Price	194-4055 $750	194-4136 $820	194-4217 $865	194-4291 $965
G	Menards SKU Discount Price	194-4068 $850	194-4149 $920	194-4220 $965	194-4301 $1065
H	Menards SKU Discount Price	194-4071 $945	194-4152 $1015	194-4233 $1060	194-4314 $1160

Many of our plans are available in CAD. For availability, call or visit any **MENARDS** store and go to the Building Materials Desk.

OTHER PRODUCTS & BUILDING AIDS

MIRROR REVERSE*
Menards SKU   194-4327
Discount Price $15

ADDITIONAL SETS**
Menards SKU   194-4330
Discount Price $45

MATERIAL LIST**
Menards SKU   100-3422
Discount Price $125

EXPRESS DELIVERY
Menards SKU   194-4356
Discount Price $40

LEGAL KIT
Menards SKU   100-3422
Discount Price $35

DETAIL PLAN PACKAGES
ELECTRICAL, PLUMBING & FRAMING - ALL SAME SKU
Menards SKU   100-3422
Discount Price $20 EA.
   3 FOR $40

*See page 6
**Available only within 90 days after puchase of plan package of same plan

If at any time you feel you may need assistance in the field while building, HDA offers a technical assistance line for answering building questions pertaining to your specific plan. Please call 314-770-2228 Monday-Friday between 8:00am and 5:00pm CST and our professional design staff will be happy to help.

Please note: All blueprints are printed in response to your order, so we cannot honor requests for refunds. However, if for some reason you find that the plan you have purchased does not meet your requirements, you may exchange that plan for another plan in our collection within 90 days of purchase. At the time of the exchange, you will be charged a processing fee of 25% of your original plan package price, plus the difference in price between the plan packages (if applicable) and the cost to ship the new plans to you. Keep in mind, reproducible drawings can only be exchanged if the package is unopened and material lists can only be purchased within 90 days of purchasing the plan package.

Making Changes To Your Plan

We understand that it is difficult to find blueprints for a home that will meet all your needs. That is why HDA, Inc. (Home Design Alternatives) is pleased to offer home plan modification services.

Typical home plan modifications include:
- Changing foundation type
- Adding square footage to a plan
- Changing exterior wall framing from 2x4 to 2x6
- Changing wall heights
- Changing the entry into a garage
- Changing a two-car garage to a three-car garage or making a garage larger
- Redesigning kitchen, baths, and bedrooms
- Changing exterior elevations
- Or most other home plan modifications you may desire!

Some home plan modifications we cannot make include:
- Mirror-reversing the plans
- Adapting/engineering plans to meet local building codes
- Combining parts of two different plans
  (due to copyright laws)

Our plan modification service is easy to use. Simply:

1. Decide on the modifications you want. For the most accurate quote, be as detailed as possible and refer to rooms in the same manner as the floor plan (i.e. if the floor plan refers to a "den," use "den" in your description). Including a sketch of the modified floor plan is always helpful.

2. Visit any **MENARDS**® Building Materials Desk and request an HDA Custom Change Form.

3. Within two business days, you or your Menards store will receive your quote - that's up to you. Quotes do not include the cost of the reproducible masters required for our designer to legally make changes. For example, if your quote is $850 and the reproducible masters for your plan are $800, your order total will be $1650 including shipping and handling charges.

4. Call the number on the quote to accept and purchase the reproducible masters from the **MENARDS**® Building Materials Desk.

5. Our designer will send you up to three drafts to verify your initial changes. Extra costs apply after the third draft. If additional changes are made that alter the original request, extra charges may be incurred.

6. Once you approve a draft with the final changes, we then make the changes to the reproducible masters by adding additional sheets. The original reproducible masters (with no changes) plus your new changed sheets will be shipped to you.

Other Important Information:

- Plans cannot be redrawn in reverse format. All modifications will be made to match the reproducible master's original layout. Once you receive the plans, you can make reverse copies at your local copy shop.

- Our staff designer will provide the first draft for your review within 4 weeks (plus shipping time) of receiving your order.

- You will receive up to three drafts to review before your original changes are modified. The first draft will totally encompass all modifications based on your original request. Additional changes not included in your original request will be charged separately at an hourly rate of $75 or a flat quoted rate.

- Modifications will be drawn on a separate sheet with the changes shown and a note to see the main sheet for details. For example, a floor plan sheet from the original set (i.e. Sheet 3) would be followed by a new floor plan sheet with changes (i.e. Sheet A-3).

- Plans are drawn to meet national building codes. Modifications will not be drawn to any particular state or county codes, thus we cannot guarantee that the revisions will meet your local building codes. You may be required to have a local architect or designer review the plans in order to have them comply with your state or county building codes.

- Time and cost estimates are good for 90 calendar days.

- All modification requests need to be submitted in writing. Verbal requests will not be accepted.

Easy Steps for FAST service

Visit any **MENARDS**® Building Materials Desk and request an HDA Custom Change Form.

Simply follow the instructions to receive your quote within two business days.

Bay Ranch

Bay Window Graces Luxury Master Bedroom

1,668 total square feet of living area

Special features
- Large bay windows grace the breakfast area, master bedroom and dining room
- Extensive walk-in closets and storage spaces are located throughout the home
- Handy covered entry porch
- Large living room has a fireplace, built-in bookshelves and a sloped ceiling
- 3 bedrooms, 2 baths, 2-car drive under garage
- Basement foundation

Price Code C

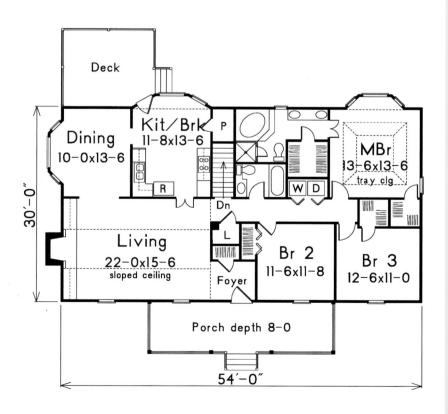

Deck

Dining
10-0x13-6

Kit/Brk
11-8x13-6

P

MBr
13-6x13-6
tray clg

30'-0"

W D

Dn

R

Living
22-0x15-6
sloped ceiling

L

Br 2
11-6x11-8

Br 3
12-6x11-0

Foyer

Porch depth 8-0

54'-0"

Kinsley

Classic Exterior Employs Innovative Planning

1,791 total square feet of living area

Special features

- ◆ Vaulted great room and octagon-shaped dining area enjoy a spectacular view of the covered patio
- ◆ Kitchen features a pass-through to the dining area, center island, large walk-in pantry and breakfast room with large bay window
- ◆ The master bedroom enjoys a vaulted ceiling and a sitting area
- ◆ The garage includes extra storage space
- ◆ 4 bedrooms, 2 baths, 2-car garage with storage
- ◆ Basement foundation, drawings also include crawl space and slab foundations

Price Code C

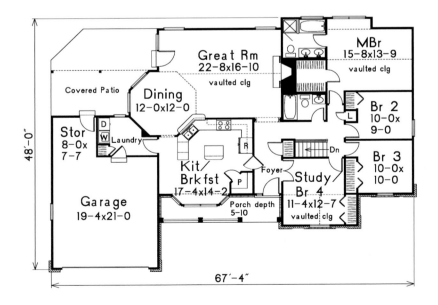

To order this plan, visit the Menards Building Materials Desk.

Summerset

Country Home With Front Orientation

2,029 total square feet of living area

Special features

◆ Stonework, gables, roof dormer and double porches create a country flavor

◆ Kitchen enjoys extravagant cabinetry and counterspace in a bay, island snack bar, built-in pantry and cheery dining area with multiple tall windows

◆ Angled stair descends from large entry with wood columns and is open to a vaulted great room with corner fireplace

◆ Master bedroom boasts two walk-in closets, a private bath with double-door entry and a secluded porch

◆ 4 bedrooms, 2 baths, 2-car side entry garage

◆ Basement foundation, drawings also include crawl space and slab foundations

Price Code D

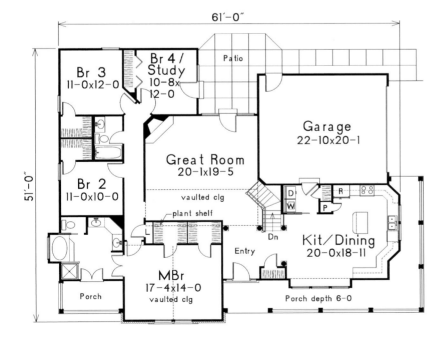

To order this plan, visit the Menards Building Materials Desk.

Mayland

Country-Style Home With Large Front Porch

1,501 total square feet of living area

Special features

◆ Spacious kitchen with dining area is open to the outdoors
◆ Convenient utility room is adjacent to the garage
◆ Master bedroom features a private bath, dressing area and access to the large covered porch
◆ Large family room creates openness
◆ 3 bedrooms, 2 baths, 2-car side entry garage
◆ Basement foundation, drawings also include crawl space and slab foundations

Price Code B

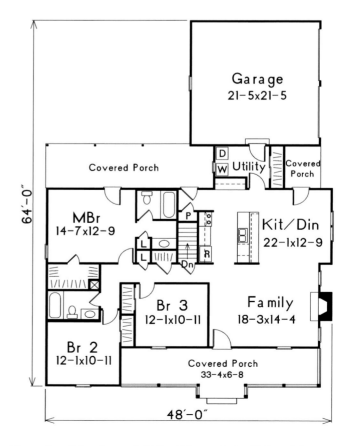

To order this plan, visit the Menards Building Materials Desk.

Delta Queen I

Layout Creates Large Open Living Area

1,285 total square feet of living area

Special features
◆ Accommodating home with ranch-style porch
◆ Large storage area on back of home
◆ Master bedroom includes dressing area, private bath and built-in bookcase
◆ Kitchen features pantry, breakfast bar and complete view to the dining room
◆ 3 bedrooms, 2 baths
◆ Crawl space foundation, drawings also include basement and slab foundations

Price Code B

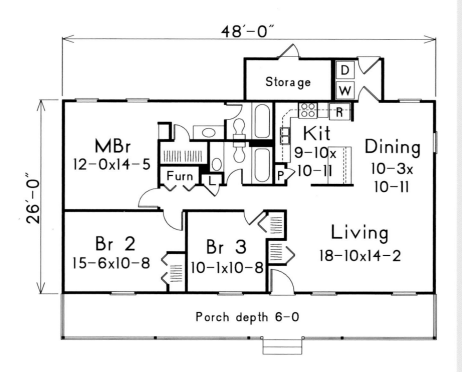

48'-0"

26'-0"

Storage

D
W

Kit
9-10x
10-11

Dining
10-3x
10-11

MBr
12-0x14-5

Furn

P
R

Br 2
15-6x10-8

Br 3
10-1x10-8

Living
18-10x14-2

Porch depth 6-0

Brookmont

Small Ranch For A Perfect Country Haven

1,761 total square feet of living area

Special features

- Exterior window dressing, roof dormers and planter boxes provide visual warmth and charm
- Great room boasts a vaulted ceiling, fireplace and opens to a pass-through kitchen
- The vaulted master bedroom includes a luxury bath and walk-in closet
- Home features eight separate closets with an abundance of storage
- 4 bedrooms, 2 baths, 2-car side entry garage
- Basement foundation

Price Code B

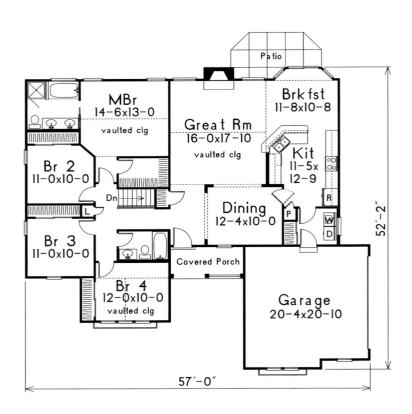

14

To order this plan, visit the Menards Building Materials Desk.

Greenfield

Private Breakfast Room Provides Casual Dining

1,708 total square feet of living area

Special features

- ◆ Massive family room is enhanced with several windows, a fireplace and access to the porch
- ◆ Deluxe master bath is accented by a step-up corner tub flanked by double vanities
- ◆ Closets throughout maintain organized living
- ◆ Bedrooms are isolated from living areas
- ◆ 3 bedrooms, 2 baths, 2-car garage
- ◆ Basement foundation, drawings also include crawl space foundation

Price Code B

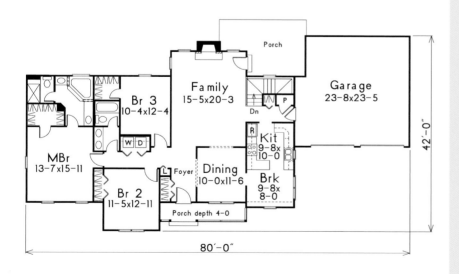

To order this plan, visit the Menards Building Materials Desk.

Ryland

Classic Ranch Has Grand Appeal With Expansive Porch

1,400 total square feet of living area

Special features

◆ Master bedroom is secluded for privacy
◆ Large utility room has additional cabinet space
◆ Covered porch provides an outdoor seating area
◆ Roof dormers add great curb appeal
◆ Living room and master bedroom feature vaulted ceilings
◆ Oversized two-car garage has storage space
◆ 3 bedrooms, 2 baths, 2-car garage
◆ Basement foundation, drawings also include crawl space foundation

Price Code B

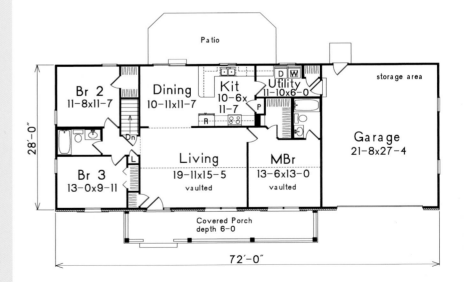

Tampa Bay

Atrium Ranch With True Pizzazz

2,397 total square feet of living area

Special features

◆ A grand entry porch leads to a dramatic vaulted foyer with plant shelf open to great room
◆ The great room enjoys a 12' vaulted ceiling, atrium featuring 2 1/2 story windows and fireplace with flanking bookshelves
◆ A conveniently located sunroom and side porch adjoin the breakfast room and garage
◆ 898 square feet of optional living area on the lower level with family room, bedroom #4 and bath
◆ 3 bedrooms, 2 baths, 3-car side entry garage
◆ Walk-out basement foundation

Price Code D

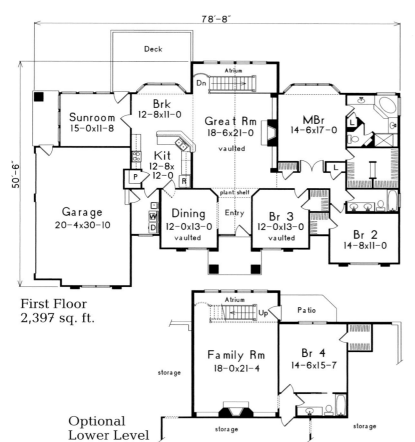

First Floor
2,397 sq. ft.

Optional
Lower Level

Mooreland

Traditional Exterior, Handsome Accents

1,882 total square feet of living area

Special features
◆ Wide, handsome entrance opens to the vaulted great room with fireplace
◆ Living and dining areas are conveniently joined but still allow privacy
◆ Private covered porch extends breakfast area
◆ Practical passageway runs through the laundry room from the garage to the kitchen
◆ Vaulted ceiling in master bedroom
◆ 3 bedrooms, 2 baths, 2-car garage
◆ Basement foundation

Price Code D

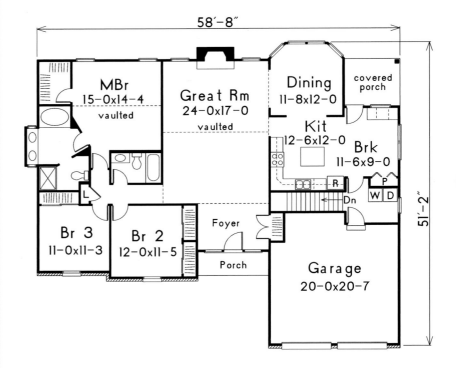

Rear View

Foxbury

Atrium's Dramatic Ambiance, Compliments Of Windows

1,721 total square feet of living area

Special features
- Roof dormers add great curb appeal
- Vaulted dining and great rooms are immersed in light from the atrium window wall
- Breakfast room opens onto the covered porch
- Functionally designed kitchen
- 3 bedrooms, 2 baths, 3-car garage
- Walk-out basement foundation, drawings also include crawl space and slab foundations
- 1,604 square feet on the first floor and 117 square feet on the lower level atrium

Price Code C

83'-0"

42'-0"

Atrium Below
Dn

Brk
11-5x12-0

Covered Porch

Great Rm
16-0x16-10
vaulted

MBr
16-0x14-0
vaulted

Kit
11-5x
12-0

vaulted

Garage
29-4x21-4

Dining
11-0x11-6

Br 3
11-1x13-3

Br 2
11-0x12-9

Porch
27-8x5-0

Brightmoore

Functional Layout For Comfortable Living

1,360 total square feet of living area

Special features

◆ Kitchen/dining room features an island workspace and plenty of dining area
◆ Master bedroom has a large walk-in closet and private bath
◆ Laundry room is adjacent to the kitchen for easy access
◆ Convenient workshop in garage
◆ Large closets in secondary bedrooms maintain organization
◆ 3 bedrooms, 2 baths, 2-car side entry garage
◆ Basement foundation, drawings also include crawl space and slab foundations

Price Code A

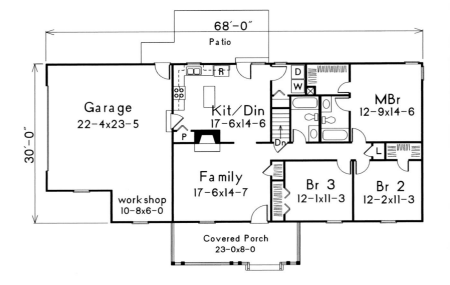

Hollybridge

Lovely, Spacious Floor Plan

1,558 total square feet of living area

Special features
- ◆ The spacious utility room is located conveniently between the garage and kitchen/dining area
- ◆ Bedrooms are separated from the living area by a hallway
- ◆ Enormous living area with fireplace and vaulted ceiling opens to the kitchen and dining area
- ◆ Master bedroom is enhanced with a large bay window, walk-in closet and private bath
- ◆ 2" x 6" exterior walls available, please order plan #M01-058D-0078
- ◆ 3 bedrooms, 2 baths, 2-car garage
- ◆ Basement foundation

Price Code B

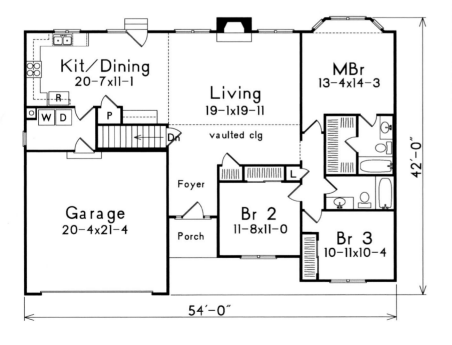

Oakridge

Central Living Area Keeps Bedrooms Private

1,546 total square feet of living area

Special features

- ◆ Spacious, open rooms create a casual atmosphere
- ◆ Master bedroom is secluded for privacy
- ◆ Dining room features a large bay window
- ◆ Kitchen and dinette combine for added space and include access to the outdoors
- ◆ Large laundry room includes a convenient sink
- ◆ 3 bedrooms, 2 baths, 2-car garage
- ◆ Basement foundation

Price Code C

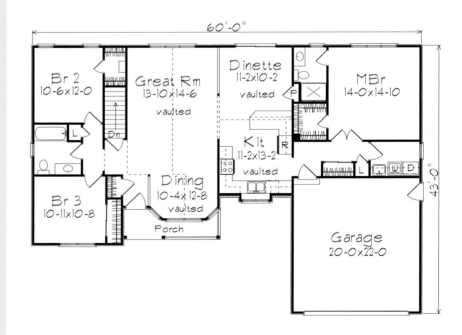

To order this plan, visit the Menards Building Materials Desk.

Ashbriar

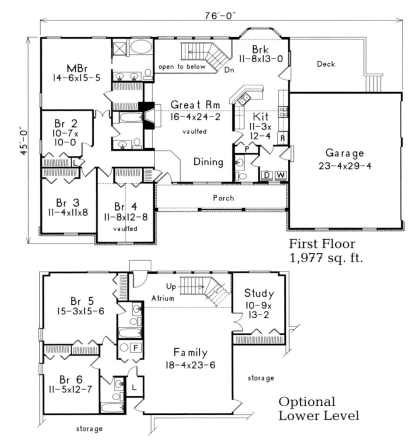

76'-0"

MBr
14-6x15-5

open to below

Brk
11-8x13-0

Dn

Deck

Great Rm
16-4x24-2
vaulted

Kit
11-3x
12-4

Br 2
10-7x
10-0

Garage
23-4x29-4

L

Dining

P

Br 3
11-4x11x8

Br 4
11-8x12-8
vaulted

Porch

D   W

45'-0"

First Floor
1,977 sq. ft.

Br 5
15-3x15-6

Up
Atrium

Study
10-9x
13-2

F

Family
18-4x23-6

storage

Br 6
11-5x12-7

L

storage

Optional
Lower Level

storage

Classic Atrium Ranch With Rooms To Spare

1,977 total square feet of living area

Special features

◆ Classic traditional exterior is always in style
◆ Spacious great room boasts a vaulted ceiling, dining area, atrium with elegant staircase and feature windows
◆ Atrium opens to 1,416 square feet of optional living area below which consists of a family room, two bedrooms, two baths and a study
◆ 4 bedrooms, 2 1/2 baths, 3-car side entry garage
◆ Walk-out basement foundation

Price Code C

To order this plan, visit the Menards Building Materials Desk.

Rockwood

Sculptured Roof Line And Facade Add Charm

1,674 total square feet of living area

Special features

- ◆ Vaulted great room, dining area and kitchen all enjoy a central fireplace and log bin
- ◆ Convenient laundry/mud room is located between the garage and the rest of the home with handy stairs to the basement
- ◆ Easily expandable screened porch and adjacent patio access the dining area
- ◆ Master bedroom features a full bath with tub, separate shower and walk-in closet
- ◆ 3 bedrooms, 2 baths, 2-car garage
- ◆ Basement foundation, drawings also include crawl space and slab foundations

Price Code B

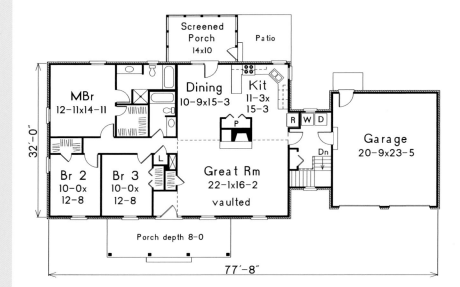

To order this plan, visit the Menards Building Materials Desk.

Burlington I

Peaceful Shaded Front Porch

1,288 total square feet of living area

Special features

◆ Kitchen, dining area and great room join to create an open living space
◆ Master bedroom includes a private bath
◆ Secondary bedrooms enjoy ample closet space
◆ Hall bath features a convenient laundry closet
◆ Dining room accesses the outdoors
◆ 3 bedrooms, 2 baths
◆ Crawl space foundation, drawings also include basement and slab foundations

Price Code A

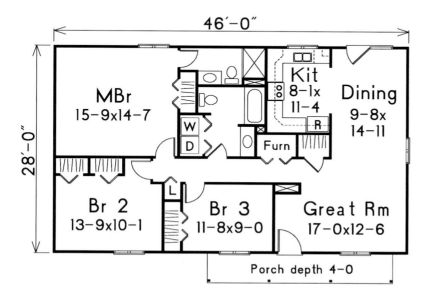

46'-0"

28'-0"

MBr
15-9x14-7

Kit
8-1x
11-4

Dining
9-8x
14-11

W
D

Furn

R

Br 2
13-9x10-1

L

Br 3
11-8x9-0

Great Rm
17-0x12-6

Porch depth 4-0

To order this plan, visit the Menards Building Materials Desk.

25

Valrico

Impressive Master Bedroom

2,287 total square feet of living area

Special features

- A double-door entry leads into an impressive master bedroom which accesses the covered porch and features a deluxe bath with double closets and a step-up tub
- Kitchen easily serves the formal and informal areas of the home
- The spacious foyer opens into formal dining and living rooms
- 4 bedrooms, 2 1/2 baths, 2-car side entry garage
- Slab foundation

Price Code E

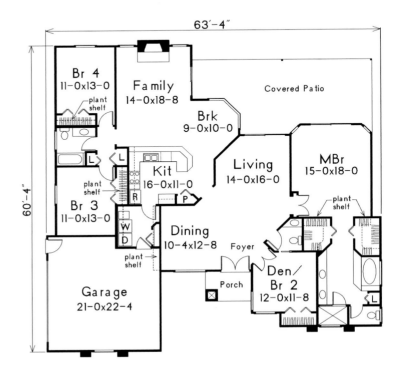

63'-4"

60'-4"

Br 4
11-0x13-0
plant shelf

Family
14-0x18-8

Covered Patio

Brk
9-0x10-0

Living
14-0x16-0

MBr
15-0x18-0

plant shelf

Kit
16-0x11-0

plant shelf

R

P

Br 3
11-0x13-0

W
D

Dining
10-4x12-8

Foyer

plant shelf

plant shelf

Garage
21-0x22-4

Porch

Den/
Br 2
12-0x11-8

L

To order this plan, visit the Menards Building Materials Desk.

Plan #M01-007D-0075

Winterbrook

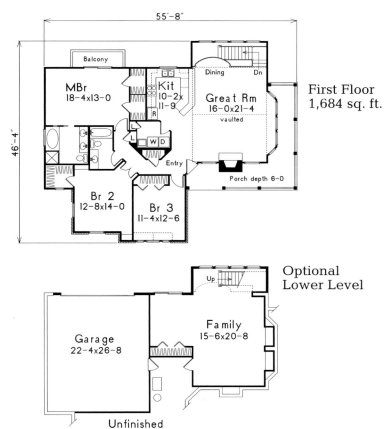

55'-8"

Balcony

MBr
18-4x13-0

Kit
10-2x
11-9

Dining   Dn

Great Rm
16-0x21-4
vaulted

First Floor
1,684 sq. ft.

46'-4"

W D

Entry

Porch depth 6-0

Br 2
12-8x14-0

Br 3
11-4x12-6

Up

Optional
Lower Level

Garage
22-4x26-8

Family
15-6x20-8

Unfinished

A Special Home For Views

1,684 total square feet of living area

Special features

◆ Delightful wrap-around porch is anchored by a full masonry fireplace
◆ The vaulted great room includes a large bay window, fireplace, dining balcony and atrium window wall
◆ Double walk-in closets, large luxury bath and sliding doors to an exterior balcony are a few fantastic features of the master bedroom
◆ Atrium opens to 611 square feet of optional living area on the lower level
◆ 3 bedrooms, 2 baths, 2-car drive under rear entry garage
◆ Walk-out basement foundation

Price Code B

To order this plan, visit the Menards Building Materials Desk.

27

Pinebluff

Well-Designed Ranch With Wrap-Around Porch

1,823 total square feet of living area

Special features

◆ Vaulted living room is spacious and easily accesses the dining area
◆ The master bedroom boasts a tray ceiling, large walk-in closet and a private bath with a corner whirlpool tub
◆ Cheerful dining area is convenient to the U-shaped kitchen and also enjoys patio access
◆ Centrally located laundry room connects the garage to the living areas
◆ 3 bedrooms, 2 baths, 2-car garage
◆ Basement foundation

Price Code C

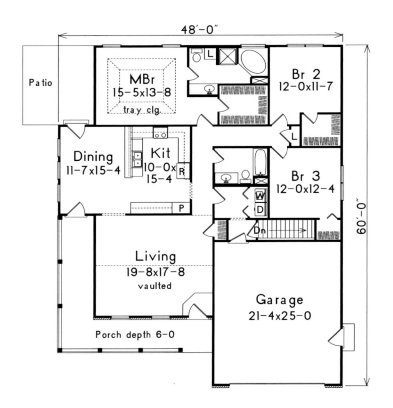

To order this plan, visit the Menards Building Materials Desk.

MENARDS

Ashley

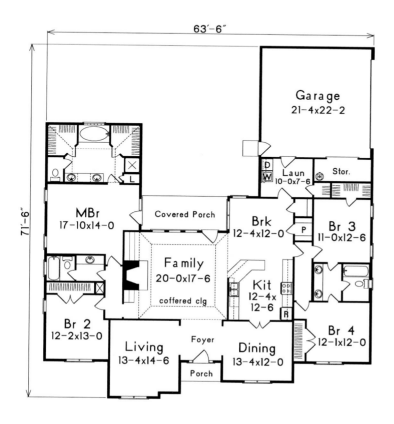

Full Windows
Grace Elegant
Family Room

2,558 total square feet of living area

Special features

- 9' ceilings throughout the home
- Angled counter in the kitchen serves the breakfast and family rooms
- The entry foyer is flanked by formal living and dining rooms
- Garage includes storage space
- 4 bedrooms, 3 baths, 2-car side entry garage
- Slab foundation, drawings also include crawl space foundation

Price Code D

To order this plan, visit the Menards Building Materials Desk.

Stonebridge

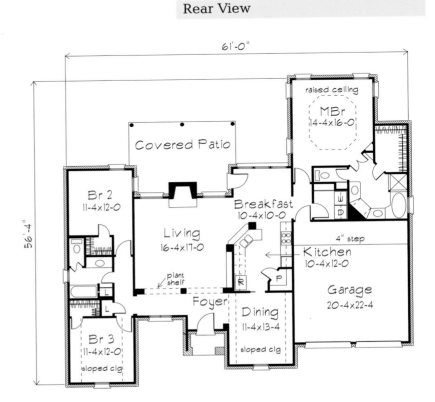

Rear View

Inviting And Cozy Covered Arched Entry

1,923 total square feet of living area

Special features

◆ The foyer opens into a spacious living room with fireplace and splendid view of the covered porch

◆ Kitchen has a walk-in pantry adjacent to the laundry area and breakfast room

◆ All bedrooms feature walk-in closets

◆ Secluded master bedroom includes unique angled bath with spacious walk-in closet

◆ 3 bedrooms, 2 baths, 2-car garage

◆ Slab foundation

Price Code C

To order this plan, visit the Menards Building Materials Desk.

Glenview

Sophisticated Ranch With Split Bedrooms

2,808 total square feet of living area

Special features

◆ An impressive front exterior showcases three porches for quiet times
◆ Large living and dining rooms flank an elegant entry
◆ Bedroom #3 shares a porch with the living room and a spacious bath with bedroom #2
◆ Vaulted master bedroom enjoys a secluded screened porch and sumptuous bath with corner tub, double vanities and huge walk-in closet
◆ Living room can easily convert to an optional fourth bedroom
◆ 3 bedrooms, 2 1/2 baths, 3-car side entry garage
◆ Basement foundation

Price Code F

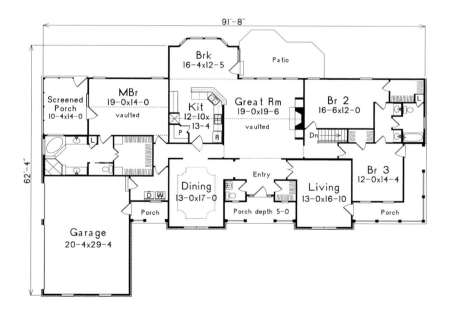

Stratford

Vaulted Ceilings Add Light And Dimension

1,676 total square feet of living area

Special features

◆ The living area skylights and large breakfast room with bay window provide plenty of sunlight
◆ The master bedroom has a walk-in closet and both the secondary bedrooms have large closets
◆ Vaulted ceilings, plant shelving and a fireplace provide a quality living area
◆ 3 bedrooms, 2 baths, 2-car garage
◆ Basement foundation, drawings also include crawl space and slab foundations

Price Code B

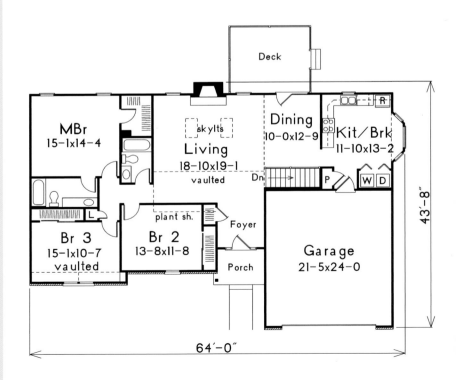

To order this plan, visit the Menards Building Materials Desk.

Evergreen

Great Room Forms Core Of This Home

2,076 total square feet of living area

Special features
- ◆ Vaulted great room has a fireplace flanked by windows and skylights that welcome the sun
- ◆ Kitchen leads to the vaulted breakfast room and rear deck
- ◆ Study located off the foyer provides a great location for a home office
- ◆ Large bay windows grace the master bedroom and bath
- ◆ 3 bedrooms, 2 baths, 2-car garage
- ◆ Basement foundation

Price Code C

Deck

Great Room
20-7x17-8
vaulted
skylts

skylt

MBr
16-0x12-0
vaulted
plant shelf

Breakfast
12-3x10-0
vaulted

plant shelf

Br 2
10-0x10-5

Kit
12-11x12-0

Dn

plant shelf

Dining
12-0x14-0

Foyer

Study
12-0x12-6

Br 3
13-5x10-0

Porch

Garage
19-4x19-4

51'-8"

63'-0"

To order this plan, visit the Menards Building Materials Desk.

Bradley

See-Through Fireplace Joins Gathering Rooms

1,684 total square feet of living area

Special features

◆ The bayed dining area boasts convenient double-door access onto the large deck

◆ The family room features several large windows for brightness

◆ Bedrooms are separate from living areas for privacy

◆ Master bedroom offers a bath with walk-in closet, double-bowl vanity and both a shower and a whirlpool tub

◆ 3 bedrooms, 2 1/2 baths, 2-car garage

◆ Basement foundation

Price Code B

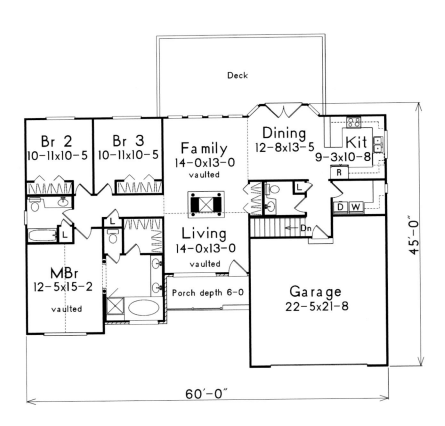

Deck

Br 2
10-11x10-5

Br 3
10-11x10-5

Family
14-0x13-0
vaulted

Dining
12-8x13-5

Kit
9-3x10-8

MBr
12-5x15-2
vaulted

Living
14-0x13-0
vaulted

Porch depth 6-0

Garage
22-5x21-8

45'-0"

60'-0"

To order this plan, visit the Menards Building Materials Desk.

Alexander

Dramatic Roof Line Accents This Ranch

2,260 total square feet of living area

Special features

◆ Luxurious master bedroom includes a raised ceiling, bath with oversized tub, separate shower and large walk-in closet
◆ Convenient kitchen and breakfast area with ample pantry storage
◆ Formal foyer leads into large living room with warming fireplace
◆ Convenient secondary entrance for everyday traffic
◆ 3 bedrooms, 2 baths, 2-car garage
◆ Slab foundation

Price Code D

79'-0"

54'-8"

MBr
13-4x16-0
raised clg

Brk
12-0x11-0

Br 3
13-4x11-4

Living
17-0x21-4

Kit
12-0x
12-0

Garage
21-4x21-0

W D
sink

P R

Foyer

Dining
13-4x11-8
sloped clg

Br 2
13-4x12-0

Study
11-4x12-0

Porch

To order this plan, visit the Menards Building Materials Desk.

Briarwood

Enchanting Country Cottage

1,140 total square feet of living area

Special features

◆ Open and spacious living and dining areas for family gatherings

◆ Well-organized kitchen has an abundance of cabinetry and a built-in pantry

◆ Roomy master bath features a double-bowl vanity

◆ 3 bedrooms, 2 baths, 2-car drive under garage

◆ Basement foundation

Price Code AA

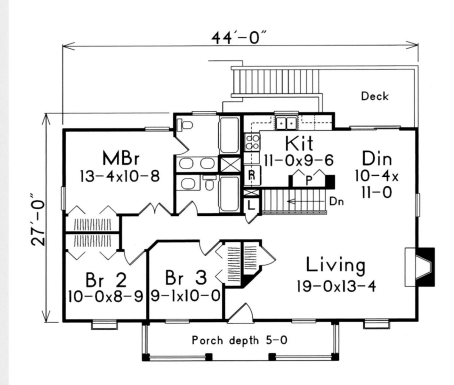

To order this plan, visit the Menards Building Materials Desk.

Rosebriar

Well-Designed Floor Plan Has Many Extras

2,437 total square feet of living area

Special features

- Spacious breakfast area with access to the covered porch is adjacent to the kitchen and great room
- Elegant dining area has a columned entrance and built-in corner cabinets
- Cozy study has a handsome double-door entrance off a large foyer
- A raised ceiling and lots of windows in the master bedroom create a spacious, open feel
- 3 bedrooms, 2 baths, 2-car side entry garage
- Slab foundation, drawings also include crawl space foundation

Price Code D

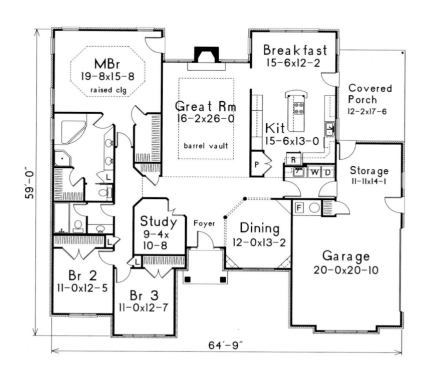

MENARDS

Southfield

Graciously Designed Traditional Ranch

1,477 total square feet of living area

Special features

◆ Oversized porch provides protection from the elements

◆ Innovative kitchen employs step-saving design

◆ Kitchen has a snack bar which opens to the breakfast room with bay window

◆ 2" x 6" exterior walls available, please order plan #M01-058D-0081

◆ 3 bedrooms, 2 baths, 2-car side entry garage with storage area

◆ Basement foundation

Price Code A

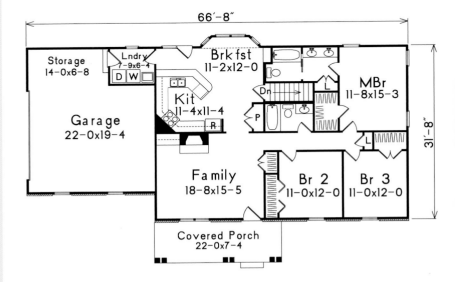

To order this plan, visit the Menards Building Materials Desk.

Saxony II

Stylish Ranch With Rustic Charm

1,344 total square feet of living area

Special features
- ◆ Family/dining room has sliding glass doors to the outdoors
- ◆ Master bedroom features a private bath
- ◆ Hall bath includes a double-bowl vanity for added convenience
- ◆ U-shaped kitchen features a large pantry and laundry area
- ◆ 3 bedrooms, 2 baths, 2-car garage
- ◆ Crawl space foundation, drawings also include basement and slab foundations

Price Code A

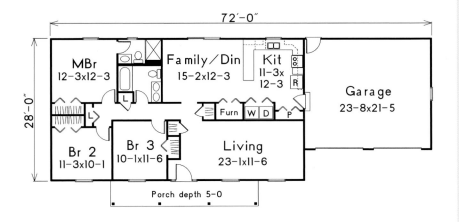

72'-0"

28'-0"

MBr
12-3x12-3

Family/Din
15-2x12-3

Kit
11-3x
12-3

Garage
23-8x21-5

Furn W D P

Br 2
11-3x10-1

Br 3
10-1x11-6

Living
23-1x11-6

Porch depth 5-0

Oasis

A Spectacular Showplace

4,826 total square feet of living area

Special features

- ◆ Brightly lit entry connects to great room with balcony and massive bay-shaped atrium
- ◆ Kitchen has island/snack bar, walk-in pantry, computer area and an atrium overlook
- ◆ Master bedroom has sitting area, walk-in closets, atrium overlook and luxury bath with private courtyard
- ◆ Family room/atrium, home theater area with wet bar, game room and guest bedroom comprise the lower level
- ◆ 4 bedrooms, 3 1/2 baths, 3-car side entry garage
- ◆ Walk-out basement foundation with lawn and garden workroom

Price Code G

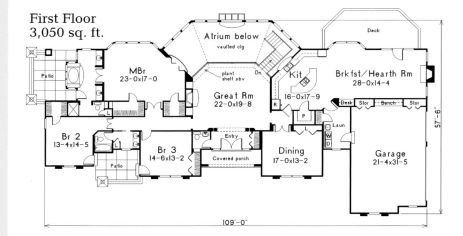

Great Room/Atrium

First Floor
3,050 sq. ft.

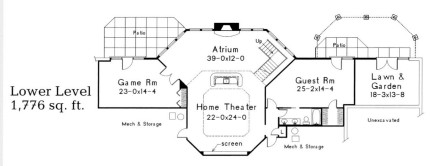

Lower Level
1,776 sq. ft.

To order this plan, visit the Menards Building Materials Desk.

Plan #M01-068D-0010

MENARDS

Spring Hill

Bedrooms Separate From Rest Of Home

1,849 total square feet of living area

Special features
- Enormous laundry/mud room has many extras including a storage area and half bath
- Lavish master bath has a corner whirlpool tub, double sinks, separate shower and walk-in closet
- Secondary bedrooms include walk-in closets
- Kitchen has a wrap-around eating counter and is positioned between the formal dining area and breakfast room for convenience
- 3 bedrooms, 2 1/2 baths, 2-car side entry garage
- Slab foundation, drawings also include crawl space foundation

Price Code C

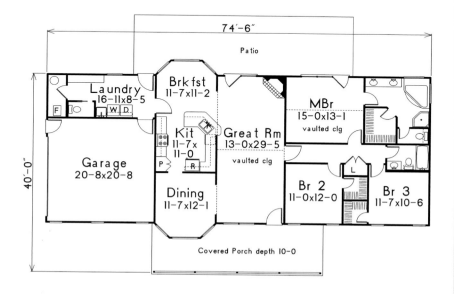

74'-6"

Patio

Laundry 16-11x8-5

Brkfst 11-7x11-2

MBr 15-0x13-1 vaulted clg

Kit 11-7x 11-0

Great Rm 13-0x29-5 vaulted clg

Garage 20-8x20-8

40'-0"

Dining 11-7x12-1

Br 2 11-0x12-0

Br 3 11-7x10-6

Covered Porch depth 10-0

To order this plan, visit the Menards Building Materials Desk.

MENARDS

Dexter

Compact Home Is Charming And Functional

1,404 total square feet of living area

Special features

- ◆ Split-foyer entrance
- ◆ Bayed living area features a unique vaulted ceiling and fireplace
- ◆ Wrap-around kitchen has corner windows for added sunlight and a bar that overlooks the dining area
- ◆ Master bath features a garden tub with separate shower
- ◆ Rear deck provides handy access to the dining room and kitchen
- ◆ 3 bedrooms, 2 baths, 2-car drive under garage
- ◆ Basement foundation, drawings also include partial crawl space foundation

Price Code A

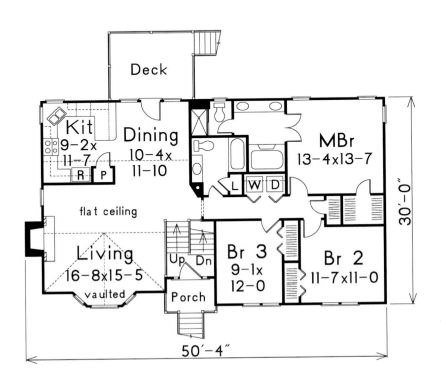

To order this plan, visit the Menards Building Materials Desk.

Dayton

Vaulted Ceiling Frames Circle-Top Window

1,195 total square feet of living area

Special features
◆ Dining room opens onto the patio
◆ Master bedroom features a vaulted ceiling, private bath and walk-in closet
◆ Coat closets are located by both the entrances
◆ Convenient secondary entrance is located at the back of the garage
◆ 3 bedrooms, 2 baths, 2-car garage
◆ Basement foundation

Price Code AA

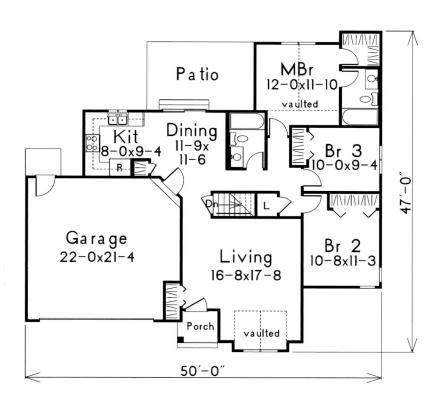

To order this plan, visit the Menards Building Materials Desk.

43

Plan #M01-007D-0062

MENARDS

Carlston

Classic Elegance

2,483 total square feet of living area

Special features

- ◆ A large entry porch with open brick arches and palladian door welcomes guests
- ◆ The vaulted great room features an entertainment center alcove and the ideal layout for furniture placement
- ◆ The dining room is extra large with a stylish tray ceiling
- ◆ A convenient kitchen with wrap-around counter, menu desk and pantry opens to the cozy breakfast area
- ◆ 4 bedrooms, 2 baths, 2-car side entry garage
- ◆ Basement foundation

Price Code D

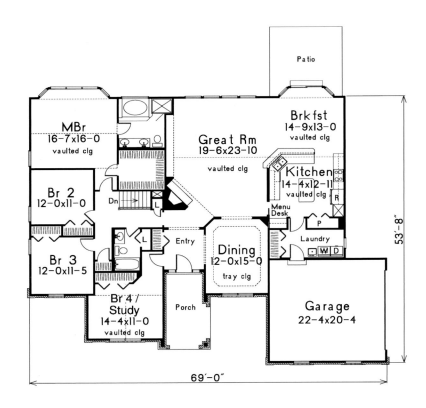

44

To order this plan, visit the Menards Building Materials Desk.

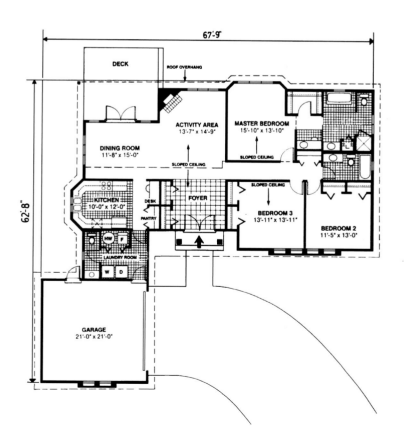

Riviera

Casual Ranch

1,960 total square feet of living area

Special features

- ◆ Comforts abound in this well-designed ranch
- ◆ Sunlit entryway leads to activity area with corner fireplace at rear of home
- ◆ U-shaped kitchen with built-in pantry and desk is adjacent to the dining room with an optional deck
- ◆ Large laundry room with a half bath is conveniently located adjacent to the garage and just off the kitchen
- ◆ Master bedroom features a large walk-in closet, dressing area with makeup vanity and compartmented bath with shower and raised tub
- ◆ Two additional bedrooms are served with a full bath
- ◆ 3 bedrooms, 2 1/2 baths, 2-car side entry garage
- ◆ Slab foundation

Price Code C

To order this plan, visit the Menards Building Materials Desk.

MENARDS

Sycamore

Open Ranch Design Gives Expansive Look

1,630 total square feet of living area

Special features

◆ Crisp facade and full windows front and back offer open viewing
◆ Wrap-around rear deck is accessible from the breakfast room, dining room and master bedroom
◆ Vaulted ceilings top the living room and master bedroom
◆ Sitting area and large walk-in closet complement the master bedroom
◆ 3 bedrooms, 2 baths, 2-car garage
◆ Basement foundation

Price Code B

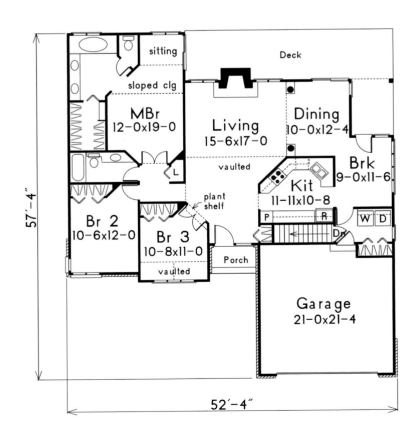

To order this plan, visit the Menards Building Materials Desk.

Darlington

Raised Foyer And Archways Create An Impressive Entry

2,070 total square feet of living area

Special features

- ◆ Energy efficient home with 2" x 6" exterior walls
- ◆ Access the rear deck through the nook area
- ◆ Master bedroom features an arched entrance into the bath with a separate shower and tub, dressing area and walk-in closet
- ◆ Sunken family room enjoys a fireplace
- ◆ 3 bedrooms, 2 baths, 2-car garage
- ◆ Basement foundation, drawings also include slab and crawl space foundations

Price Code C

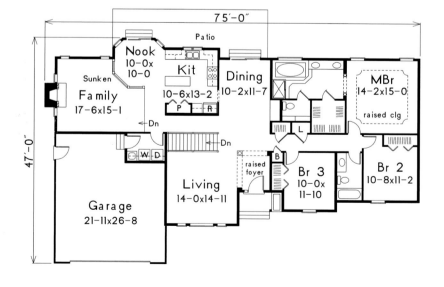

To order this plan, visit the Menards Building Materials Desk.

Plan #M01-007D-0008

Westport

Charming Design Features Home Office

2,452 total square feet of living area

Special features

◆ Cheery and spacious home office room with private entrance and bath, two closets, vaulted ceiling and transomed window is perfect shown as a home office or a fourth bedroom

◆ Great room features a vaulted ceiling, fireplace, extra storage closets and patio doors to sundeck

◆ Extra-large kitchen features walk-in pantry, cooktop island and bay window

◆ Vaulted master bedroom includes transomed windows, walk-in closet and luxurious bath

◆ 3 bedrooms, 2 1/2 baths, 3-car garage

◆ Basement foundation

Price Code D

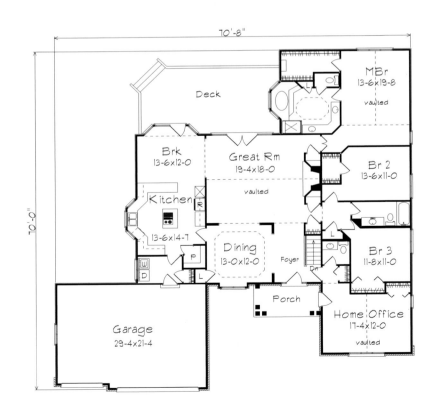

To order this plan, visit the Menards Building Materials Desk.

Charlene

Columns Grace The Interior And Exterior

1,476 total square feet of living area

Special features
- ◆ Energy efficient home with 2" x 6" exterior walls
- ◆ Living room is made more spacious by a vaulted ceiling
- ◆ Laundry/mud room has a large pantry and accesses the dining area, garage, stairs and the outdoors
- ◆ Master bedroom features a bath and private deck
- ◆ Dining room is defined by columns and a large bow window
- ◆ 3 bedrooms, 2 baths, 2-car side entry garage
- ◆ Basement foundation, drawings also include slab foundation

Price Code B

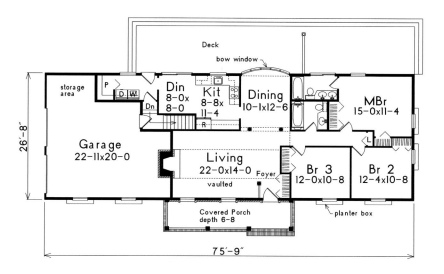

To order this plan, visit the Menards Building Materials Desk.

Baldwin

Exciting Split-Foyer Entrance

1,407 total square feet of living area

Special features

- ◆ Large living room has a fireplace and access to the rear deck
- ◆ Kitchen and dining area combine to create an open gathering area
- ◆ Convenient laundry room and broom closet
- ◆ Master bedroom includes a private bath with large vanity and separate tub and shower
- ◆ 3 bedrooms, 2 baths, 2-car drive under garage
- ◆ Basement foundation

Price Code A

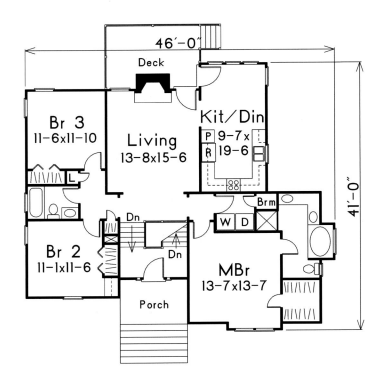

To order this plan, visit the Menards Building Materials Desk.

Bethany

Colossal Great Room

1,599 total square feet of living area

Special features

- ◆ Efficiently designed kitchen includes a large pantry and easy access to the laundry room
- ◆ Bedroom #3 has a charming window seat
- ◆ Master bedroom has a full bath and large walk-in closet
- ◆ 4 bedrooms, 2 baths, 2-car garage
- ◆ Basement foundation, drawings also include crawl space and slab foundations

Price Code B

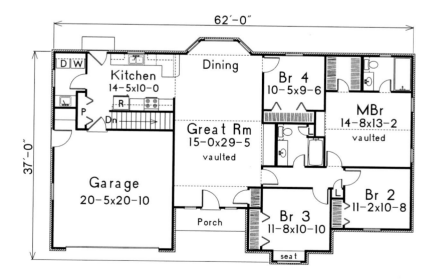

62'-0"

37'-0"

D|W

Kitchen
14-5x10-0

Dining

Br 4
10-5x9-6

MBr
14-8x13-2
vaulted

P

R

Dn

Great Rm
15-0x29-5
vaulted

Garage
20-5x20-10

Br 2
11-2x10-8

Porch

Br 3
11-8x10-10

seat

Wynehaven

Fountain Graces Entry

2,397 total square feet of living area

Special features

◆ Covered entrance with fountain leads to the double-door entry and foyer

◆ Kitchen features two pantries and opens into the breakfast and family rooms

◆ Master bath features a huge walk-in closet, electric clothes carousel, double-bowl vanity and corner tub

◆ 3 bedrooms, 2 1/2 baths, 2-car garage

◆ Slab foundation

Price Code E

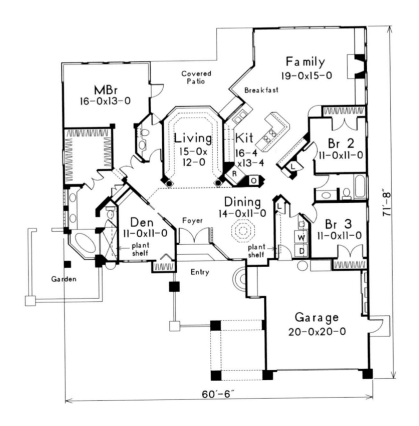

To order this plan, visit the Menards Building Materials Desk.

Santa Clara

Distinctive Ranch Has A Larger Look

1,360 total square feet of living area

Special features
◆ Double-gabled front facade frames large windows
◆ The foyer opens to the vaulted great room with a fireplace and access to the rear deck
◆ Vaulted ceiling and large windows add openness to the kitchen/ breakfast room
◆ Bedroom #3 easily converts to a den
◆ Plan easily adapts to crawl space or slab construction, with the utilities replacing the stairs
◆ 3 bedrooms, 2 baths, 2-car garage
◆ Basement foundation

Price Code A

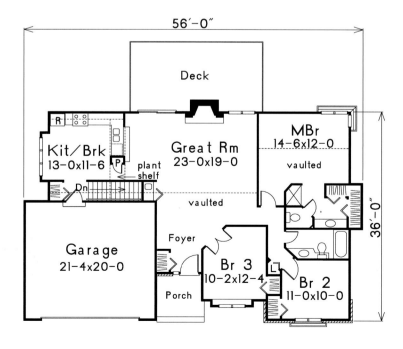

Le Chateau

Spacious One-Story With French Country Flavor

2,695 total square feet of living area

Special features

- ◆ A grand-scale great room features a fireplace with flanking shelves, handsome entry foyer with staircase and opens to a large kitchen and breakfast room
- ◆ Roomy master bedroom has a bay window, huge walk-in closet and bath
- ◆ Bedrooms #2 and #3 are generously oversized with walk-in closets and a Jack and Jill style bath
- ◆ 3 bedrooms, 2 1/2 baths, 2-car side entry garage
- ◆ Basement foundation

Price Code E

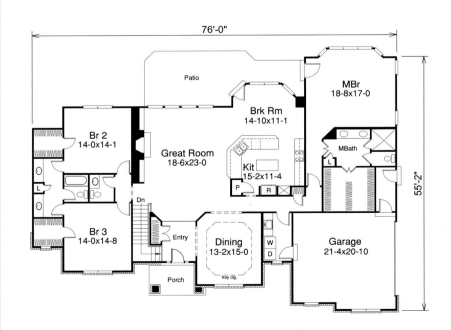

To order this plan, visit the Menards Building Materials Desk.

Joneberry

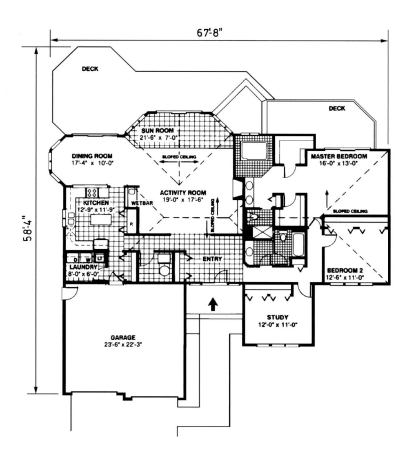

Sunny Retreat

2,180 total square feet of living area

Special features

◆ Exterior provides eye-catching roof lines

◆ Entry has a cathedral ceiling and leads to the activity room which features vaulted ceilings, sunken sun room and wet bar

◆ Master bedroom has dual walk-in closets, raised tub and compartmented shower

◆ Front-facing study with closet would make a perfect office or third bedroom

◆ 2 bedrooms, 2 baths, 2-car garage

◆ Crawl space foundation

Price Code C

To order this plan, visit the Menards Building Materials Desk.

Ashland

Layout Features All The Essentials For Comfortable Living

1,344 total square feet of living area

Special features
◆ Kitchen has side entry, laundry area, pantry and joins family/dining area
◆ Master bedroom includes a private bath
◆ Linen and storage closets in hall
◆ Covered porch opens to the spacious living room with a handy coat closet
◆ 3 bedrooms, 2 baths
◆ Crawl space foundation, drawings also include basement and slab foundations

Price Code A

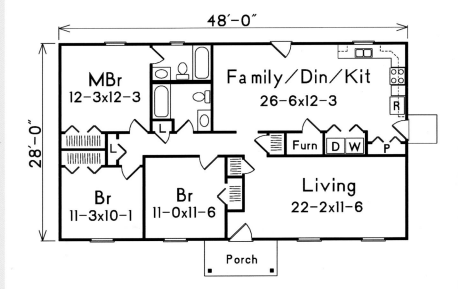

48'-0"

28'-0"

MBr
12-3x12-3

Family/Din/Kit
26-6x12-3

L

Furn D W P

Br
11-3x10-1

Br
11-0x11-6

Living
22-2x11-6

Porch

MENARDS

Hanna

Spectacular View From The Great Room

3,796 total square feet of living area

Special features
◆ Entry foyer leads directly to the great room with a fireplace and wonderful view through a wall of windows
◆ Kitchen and breakfast area feature a large island cooktop, pantry and easy access outdoors
◆ Master bedroom includes a vaulted ceiling and pocket door entrance into the master bath that features a double-bowl vanity and large tub
◆ 4 bedrooms, 3 1/2 baths, 2-car garage
◆ Basement foundation

Price Code F

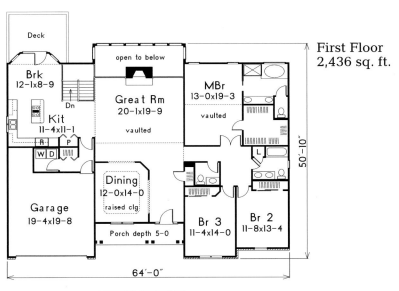

First Floor 2,436 sq. ft.

Deck

Brk 12-1x8-9

open to below

Great Rm 20-1x19-9 vaulted

Dn

Kit 11-4x11-1

MBr 13-0x19-3 vaulted

R P
W D

Dining 12-0x14-0 raised clg

Garage 19-4x19-8

Br 3 11-4x14-0

Br 2 11-8x13-4

Porch depth 5-0

50'-10"

64'-0"

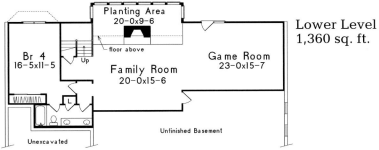

Lower Level 1,360 sq. ft.

Planting Area 20-0x9-6

floor above

Br 4 16-5x11-5

Up

Family Room 20-0x15-6

Game Room 23-0x15-7

L

Unfinished Basement

Unexcavated

To order this plan, visit the Menards Building Materials Desk.

Danville

Distinctive Turret Surrounds The Dining Bay

1,742 total square feet of living area

Special features

- ◆ Efficient kitchen combines with the breakfast area and great room creating a spacious living area
- ◆ Master bedroom includes a private bath with huge walk-in closet, shower and corner tub
- ◆ Great room boasts a fireplace and access outdoors
- ◆ Laundry room is conveniently located near the kitchen and garage
- ◆ 3 bedrooms, 2 baths, 2-car garage
- ◆ Slab foundation, drawings also include crawl space foundation

Price Code B

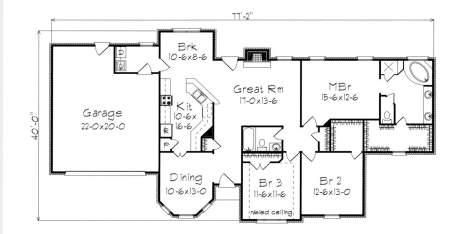

To order this plan, visit the Menards Building Materials Desk.

Bakersville

Dormers And Stone Veneer Add Exterior Appeal

1,609 total square feet of living area

Special features

- ◆ Efficient kitchen includes a corner pantry and adjacent laundry room
- ◆ Breakfast room boasts plenty of windows and opens onto a rear deck
- ◆ Master bedroom features a tray ceiling and private deluxe bath
- ◆ Entry opens into large living area with fireplace
- ◆ 4 bedrooms, 2 baths, 2-car garage
- ◆ Basement foundation

Price Code B

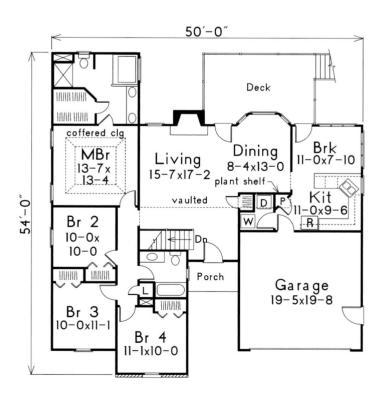

Altamont

Rambling Ranch Has Luxurious Master Bedroom

2,523 total square feet of living area

Special features

◆ Entry with high ceiling leads to massive vaulted great room with wet bar, plant shelves, pillars and fireplace with a harmonious window trio

◆ Elaborate kitchen with bay and breakfast bar adjoins morning room with fireplace-in-a-bay

◆ Vaulted master bedroom features a fireplace, book and plant shelves, large walk-in closet and double baths

◆ 3 bedrooms, 2 baths, 3-car garage

◆ Basement foundation

Price Code D

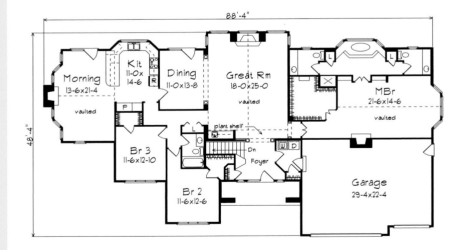

To order this plan, visit the Menards Building Materials Desk.

Ramsbury

Garden Courtyard Lends Distinction And Privacy

1,996 total square feet of living area

Special features

◆ Garden courtyard comes with a large porch and direct access to the master bedroom suite, breakfast room and garage
◆ Sculptured entrance has artful plant shelves and special niche in foyer
◆ Master bedroom boasts French doors, garden tub, desk with bookshelves and generous storage
◆ Plant shelves and a high ceiling grace the hallway
◆ 3 bedrooms, 2 baths, 2-car side entry garage
◆ Slab foundation, drawings also include crawl space foundation

Price Code D

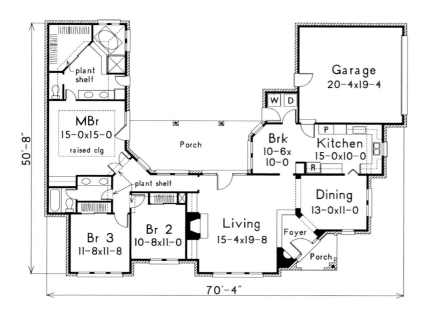

Forestville

Covered Porch Adds Charm To Entrance

1,655 total square feet of living area

Special features
◆ Master bedroom features a 9' ceiling, walk-in closet and bath with dressing area
◆ Oversized family room includes a 10' ceiling and masonry see-through fireplace
◆ Island kitchen has convenient access to the laundry room
◆ Handy covered walkway from the garage leads to the kitchen and dining area
◆ 3 bedrooms, 2 baths, 2-car garage
◆ Crawl space foundation

Price Code B

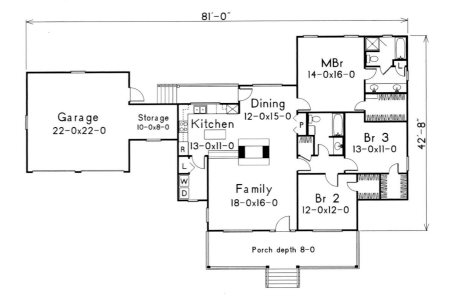

To order this plan, visit the Menards Building Materials Desk.

Rosebury

Basic Serenity

1,102 total square feet of living area

Special features
- ◆ Compact design with a dressy exterior
- ◆ Spacious living room with separate entry and coat closet
- ◆ Eat-in kitchen with first floor laundry
- ◆ Master bedroom and second bedroom share a roomy full bath
- ◆ 2 bedrooms, 1 bath, 2-car garage
- ◆ Basement foundation, drawings also include crawl space foundation

Price Code AA

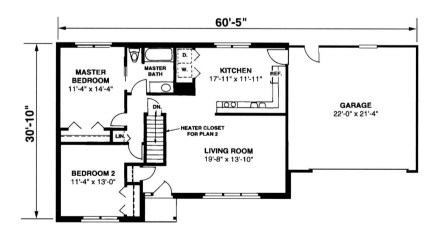

Davidson

Cheerful And Sunny Kitchen

1,540 total square feet of living area

Special features

◆ Porch entrance into foyer leads to an impressive dining area with a full window and a half-circle window above

◆ Kitchen/breakfast room features a center island and cathedral ceiling

◆ Great room with cathedral ceiling and exposed beams is accessible from the foyer

◆ Master bedroom includes a full bath and walk-in closet

◆ Two additional bedrooms share a full bath

◆ 3 bedrooms, 2 baths, 2-car garage

◆ Basement foundation, drawings also include crawl space and slab foundations

Price Code B

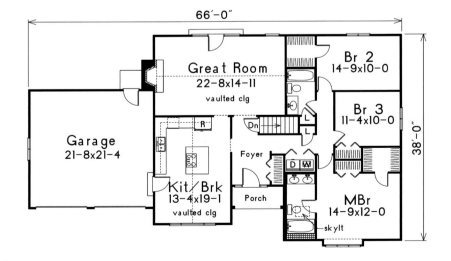

To order this plan, visit the Menards Building Materials Desk.

Creston

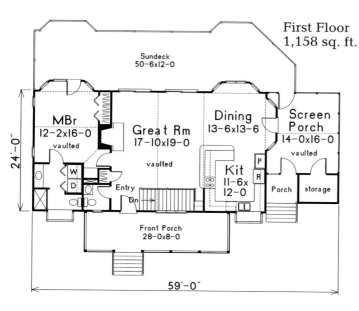

First Floor
1,158 sq. ft.

Sundeck
50-6x12-0

MBr
12-2x16-0
vaulted

Great Rm
17-10x19-0
vaulted

Dining
13-6x13-6

Screen
Porch
14-0x16-0
vaulted

24'-0"

W
D

Kit
11-6x
12-0

P
R

Entry
Dn

Porch   storage

Front Porch
28-0x8-0

59'-0"

Lower Level
574 sq. ft.

Garage
19-6x23-4

Br 2
11-8x11-6

Br 3
12-6x11-6

Up

Stor

Large Sundeck Creates Outdoor Living Area

1,732 total square feet of living area

Special features

◆ Spacious great room has a vaulted ceiling and fireplace that overlooks the large sundeck

◆ Dramatic dining room boasts extensive windows and angled walls

◆ Vaulted master bedroom includes a private bath with laundry area and accesses the sundeck

◆ Convenient second entrance leads to the screen porch and dining area

◆ 3 bedrooms, 2 1/2 baths, 2-car drive under garage

◆ Basement foundation

Price Code B

To order this plan, visit the Menards Building Materials Desk.

65

Townsley

Circle-Top Windows Grace The Facade Of This Home

1,672 total square feet of living area

Special features

◆ Vaulted master bedroom features a walk-in closet and adjoining bath with separate tub and shower
◆ Energy efficient home with 2" x 6" exterior walls
◆ Covered front and rear porches
◆ 12' ceilings in the living room, kitchen and bedroom #2
◆ Kitchen is complete with a pantry, angled bar and adjacent eating area
◆ Sloped ceiling in the dining room
◆ 3 bedrooms, 2 baths, 2-car side entry garage
◆ Crawl space foundation, drawings also include basement and slab foundations

Price Code C

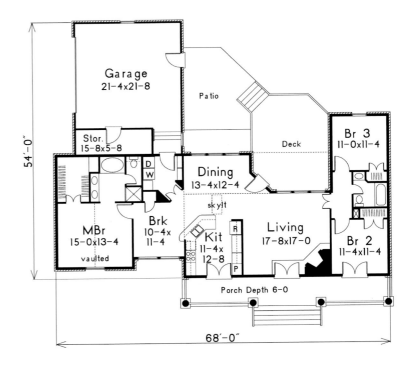

66

Kentland

Provides Family Living At Its Best

1,993 total square feet of living area

Special features
◆ Spacious country kitchen boasts a fireplace and plenty of natural light from windows
◆ Formal dining room features a large bay window and steps down to the sunken living room
◆ Master bedroom features corner windows, plant shelves and a deluxe private bath
◆ Entry opens into the vaulted living room with windows flanking the fireplace
◆ 3 bedrooms, 2 baths, 2-car garage
◆ Basement foundation

Price Code D

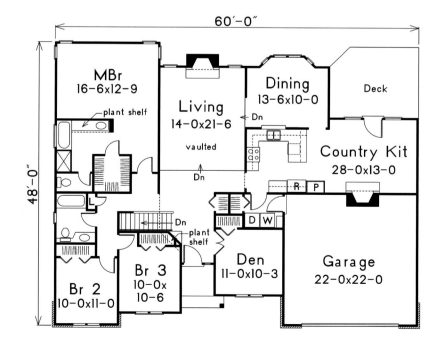

Maple Hill

Ranch Offers Country Elegance

1,787 total square feet of living area

Special features

- Large great room with fireplace and vaulted ceiling features three large skylights and windows galore
- Cooking is sure to be a pleasure in this L-shaped well-appointed kitchen which includes a bayed breakfast area with access to the rear deck
- Every bedroom offers a spacious walk-in closet with a convenient laundry room just steps away
- 415 square feet of optional living area available on the lower level
- 3 bedrooms, 2 baths, 2-car drive under garage
- Walk-out basement foundation

Price Code B

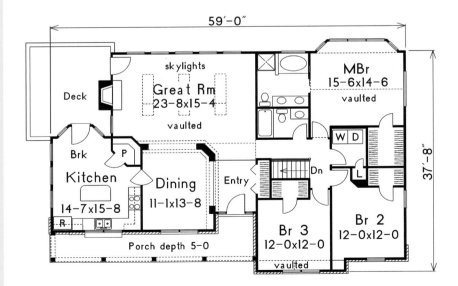

To order this plan, visit the Menards Building Materials Desk.

Augustine

Ultimate Family Design

2,072 total square feet of living area

Special features

◆ Energy efficient home with 2" x 6" exterior walls
◆ Hip roofs and an arched window create a stunning facade
◆ The kitchen, living and dining rooms combine for the ultimate gathering spot and enjoy a fireplace, built-in shelves, a bay window and access to the deck
◆ The amazing master bedroom enjoys luxurious amenities including a bay window, walk-in closet and deluxe bath complete with a whirlpool tub
◆ 3 bedrooms, 2 1/2 baths, 3-car garage
◆ Basement foundation

Price Code C

Rosewood

Appealing Gabled Front Facade

2,412 total square feet of living area

Special features

◆ Coffered ceiling in dining room adds character and spaciousness

◆ Great room is enhanced by a vaulted ceiling and atrium window wall

◆ Spacious and well-planned kitchen includes counterspace dining and overlooks breakfast room and beyond to the deck

◆ Luxurious master bedroom features an enormous walk-in closet, private bath and easy access to the laundry area

◆ 2" x 6" exterior walls available, please order plan #M01-058D-0079

◆ 4 bedrooms, 2 baths, 3-car side entry garage

◆ Walk-out basement foundation

Price Code D

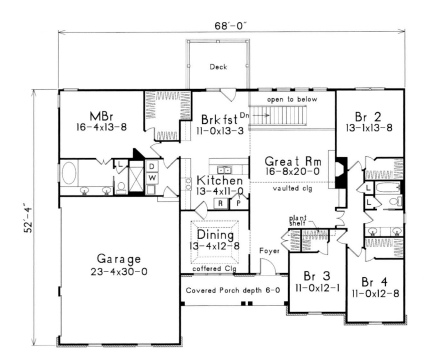

Oxford

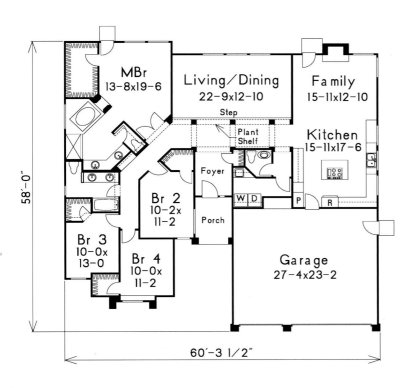

High-Styled Master Bedroom Suite

2,255 total square feet of living area

Special features

- ◆ Walk-in closets in all bedrooms
- ◆ Plant shelf graces hallway
- ◆ Large functional kitchen adjoins the family room which features a fireplace and access outdoors
- ◆ Master bath comes complete with a double vanity, enclosed toilet, separate tub and shower and cozy fireplace
- ◆ Living/dining room combine for a large formal gathering room
- ◆ 4 bedrooms, 2 1/2 baths, 3-car garage
- ◆ Slab foundation

Price Code D

Bainbridge

Upscale Ranch With Formal And Informal Areas

1,969 total square feet of living area

Special features

◆ Master bedroom boasts a luxurious bath with double sinks, two walk-in closets and an oversized tub
◆ Corner fireplace warms a conveniently located family area
◆ Formal living and dining areas in the front of the home lend a touch of privacy when entertaining
◆ Spacious utility room has counterspace and a sink
◆ 3 bedrooms, 2 baths, 2-car garage
◆ Crawl space foundation, drawings also include slab foundation

Price Code C

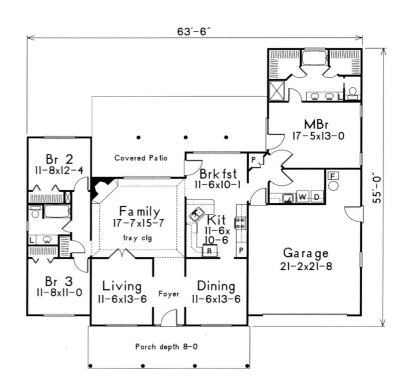

To order this plan, visit the Menards Building Materials Desk.

Medford

Wonderful Entertaining Possibilities

1,200 total square feet of living area

Special features
- ◆ Large living and dining rooms are completely open to one another with lots of space for large family gatherings
- ◆ The cozy kitchen has a half-wall open to the dining room offering lots of entertaining possibilities
- ◆ All three bedrooms have nice-sized closets and share a hall bath
- ◆ An optional second bath is available at rear of home
- ◆ 3 bedrooms, 1 bath, optional 2-car garage
- ◆ Basement foundation, drawings also include crawl space and slab foundations

Price Code A

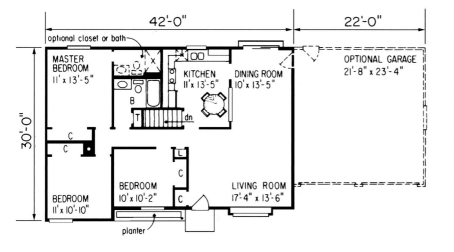

Lakeshore

Double Atrium For Fantastic Views

2,125 total square feet of living area

Special features

- A cozy porch leads to the vaulted great room with fireplace through the entry which has a walk-in closet and bath
- Large and well-arranged kitchen offers spectacular views from its cantilevered sink cabinetry through a two-story atrium window wall
- Master bedroom boasts a sitting room, large walk-in closet and bath with garden tub overhanging a brightly lit atrium
- 1,047 square feet of optional living area on the lower level featuring a study and family room with walk-in bar and full bath below the kitchen
- 3 bedrooms, 2 1/2 baths, 2-car side entry garage
- Walk-out basement foundation

Price Code C

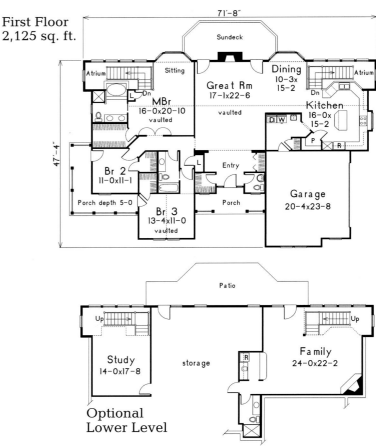

First Floor
2,125 sq. ft.

Optional
Lower Level

To order this plan, visit the Menards Building Materials Desk.

Pineview

Front Porch And Center Gable Add Style To This Ranch

988 total square feet of living area

Special features
- ◆ Pleasant covered porch entry
- ◆ The kitchen, living and dining areas are combined to maximize space
- ◆ The entry has a convenient coat closet
- ◆ Laundry closet is located adjacent to bedrooms
- ◆ 3 bedrooms, 1 bath, 1-car garage
- ◆ Basement foundation, drawings also include crawl space foundation

Price Code AA

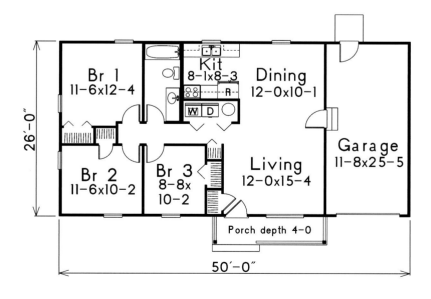

Valleybrook

Openness In A Split-Bedroom Ranch

1,574 total square feet of living area

Special features

- ◆ Foyer enters into an open great room with corner fireplace and rear dining room with adjoining kitchen
- ◆ Two secondary bedrooms share a full bath
- ◆ Master bedroom has a spacious private bath
- ◆ Garage accesses home through the spacious utility room
- ◆ 3 bedrooms, 2 baths, 2-car garage
- ◆ Basement foundation, drawings also include crawl space foundation

Price Code B

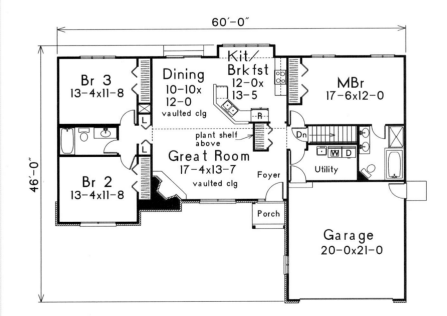

Bakersport

Traditional Ranch Home

2,015 total square feet of living area

Special features
- The foyer opens into the spacious vaulted great room
- The open kitchen/breakfast area includes an island with seating, a pantry and built-in desk
- Bedrooms remain private from living areas
- 3 bedrooms, 2 1/2 baths, 3-car side entry garage
- Basement foundation

Price Code C

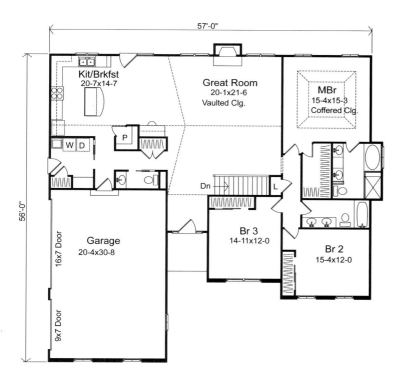

To order this plan, visit the Menards Building Materials Desk.

Springview

Vaulted Ceilings Show Off This Ranch

1,135 total square feet of living area

Special features

◆ Energy efficient home with 2" x 6" exterior walls

◆ Living and dining rooms feature vaulted ceilings and a corner fireplace

◆ Master bedroom offers a vaulted ceiling, private bath and generous closet space

◆ Compact but functional kitchen is complete with a pantry and adjacent utility room

◆ 3 bedrooms, 2 baths, 2-car garage

◆ Basement foundation, drawings also include crawl space foundation

Price Code AA

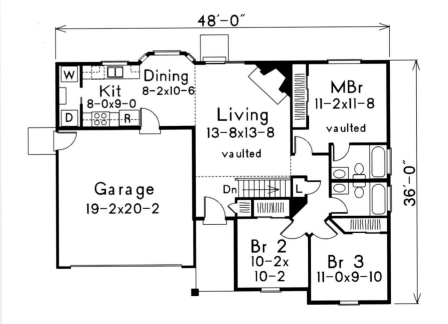

Ashwood

Stylish Features Enhance Open Living

1,846 total square feet of living area

Special features
◆ Enormous living area combines with the dining and breakfast rooms that are both complemented by extensive windows and high ceilings
◆ Master bedroom has a walk-in closet, display niche and deluxe bath
◆ Secondary bedrooms share a bath and feature large closet space and a corner window
◆ Oversized two-car garage has plenty of storage and workspace with handy access to the kitchen through the utility area
◆ Breakfast nook has wrap-around windows adding to eating enjoyment
◆ 3 bedrooms, 2 baths, 2-car garage
◆ Slab foundation

Price Code C

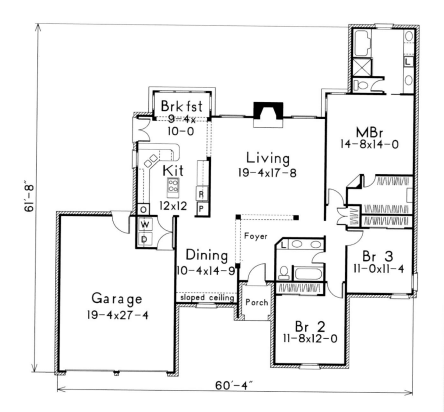

To order this plan, visit the Menards Building Materials Desk.

Mountainview

Charming Country Facade

1,643 total square feet of living area

Special features

◆ An attractive front entry porch gives this ranch a country accent

◆ Spacious family/dining room is the focal point of this design

◆ Kitchen and utility room are conveniently located near gathering areas

◆ Formal living room in the front of the home provides area for quiet and privacy

◆ Master bedroom has view to the rear of the home and a generous walk-in closet

◆ 3 bedrooms, 2 baths, 2-car garage

◆ Basement foundation, drawings also include crawl space and slab foundations

Price Code B

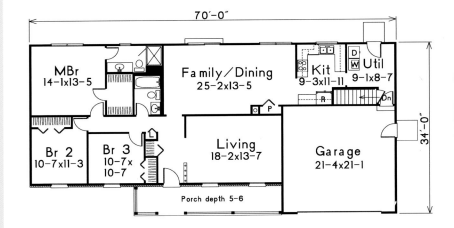

Plan #M01-007D-0065

MENARDS

Roxbury

Gracious Atrium Ranch

2,218 total square feet of living area

Special features

- ◆ Vaulted great room has an arched colonnade entry, bay windowed atrium with staircase and a fireplace
- ◆ Vaulted kitchen enjoys bay doors to deck, pass-through breakfast bar and walk-in pantry
- ◆ Breakfast room offers a bay window and snack bar open to the kitchen with a large laundry room nearby
- ◆ Atrium opens to 1,217 square feet of optional living area below
- ◆ 4 bedrooms, 2 baths, 2-car garage
- ◆ Walk-out basement foundation

Price Code D

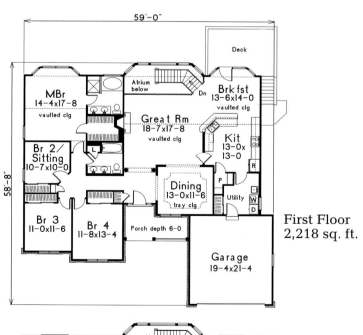

First Floor
2,218 sq. ft.

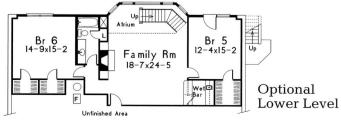

Optional
Lower Level

To order this plan, visit the Menards Building Materials Desk.

Plan #M01-001D-0001

Hearthside

Vaulted Ceilings Create Spacious Feeling

1,605 total square feet of living area

Special features

◆ Vaulted ceilings in great room, kitchen and breakfast area

◆ Spacious great room features a large bay window, fireplace, built-in bookshelves and a convenient wet bar

◆ The formal dining room and breakfast area are perfect for entertaining or everyday living

◆ Master bedroom has a spacious bath with oval tub and separate shower

◆ 3 bedrooms, 2 baths, 2-car garage

◆ Basement foundation, drawings also include slab and crawl space foundations

Price Code B

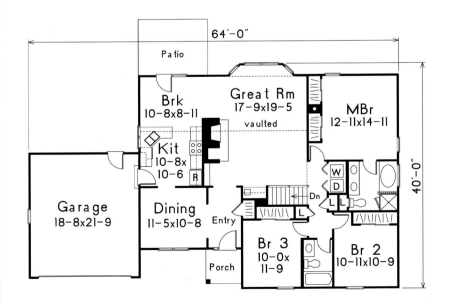

To order this plan, visit the Menards Building Materials Desk.

Plan #M01-058D-0161

MENARDS

Creektree

Built-In Shelves In The Family Room

1,993 total square feet of living area

Special features
◆ This superb ranch features an open living area with split-bedrooms
◆ An eating bar extends the kitchen connecting it to the breakfast area and family room
◆ The massive master bedroom enjoys a walk-in closet and luxurious bath
◆ 3 bedrooms, 2 baths, 2-car garage
◆ Basement foundation

Price Code AA

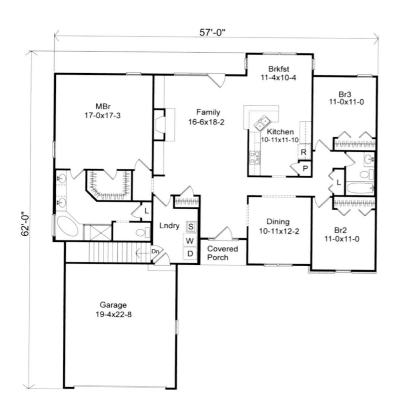

57'-0"

62'-0"

MBr
17-0x17-3

Family
16-6x18-2

Brkfst
11-4x10-4

Br3
11-0x11-0

Kitchen
10-11x11-10

R

P

L

Lndry

S
W
D

Dining
10-11x12-2

Br2
11-0x11-0

Covered
Porch

Dn

Garage
19-4x22-8

To order this plan, visit the Menards Building Materials Desk.

83

Apollo

Attractive Arched Main Entrance

2,136 total square feet of living area

Special features

◆ Vaulted breakfast nook includes bay window
◆ Kitchen is tucked away and includes a sloped ceiling and built-in pantry
◆ Large deck off activity area expands your entertaining options
◆ Master bedroom features a walk-in closet and private bath
◆ 3 bedrooms, 2 baths, 2-car garage
◆ Partial basement/crawl space foundation, drawings also include slab foundation

Price Code C

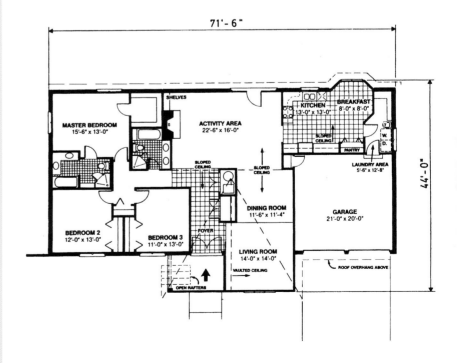

To order this plan, visit the Menards Building Materials Desk.

Countryfield

Grand-Scale Great Room In A Country Ranch

1,278 total square feet of living area

Special features

- ◆ Excellent U-shaped kitchen with garden window opens to an enormous great room with vaulted ceiling, fireplace and two skylights
- ◆ Vaulted master bedroom offers a double-door entry, access to a deck and bath and two walk-in closets
- ◆ The bath has a double-bowl vanity and dramatic step-up garden tub with a lean-to greenhouse window
- ◆ 805 square feet of optional living area on the lower level with family room, bedroom #4 and bath
- ◆ 3 bedrooms, 1 bath, 2-car garage
- ◆ Walk-out basement foundation

Price Code A

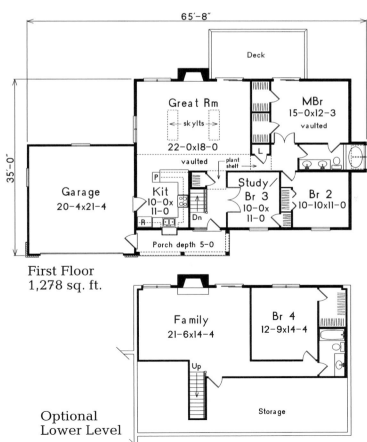

First Floor
1,278 sq. ft.

Optional
Lower Level

To order this plan, visit the Menards Building Materials Desk.

Ambsdale

Elegant Entrance To An Impressive Home

2,563 total square feet of living area

Special features

◆ Energy efficient home with 2" x 6" exterior walls

◆ Remote master bedroom features a bath with double sinks, spa tub and separate room with toilet

◆ Arched columns separate the foyer from the great room which includes a fireplace and accesses the nook

◆ Well-designed kitchen provides plenty of workspace and storage plus room for extra cooks

◆ 4 bedrooms, 2 baths, 2-car garage

◆ Basement foundation

Price Code D

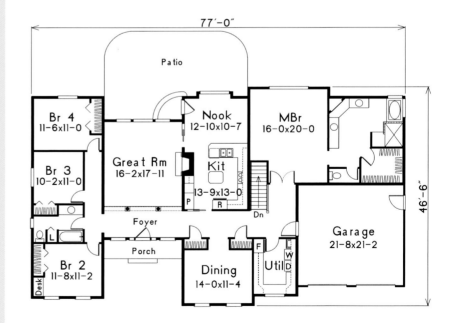

To order this plan, visit the Menards Building Materials Desk.

Collison

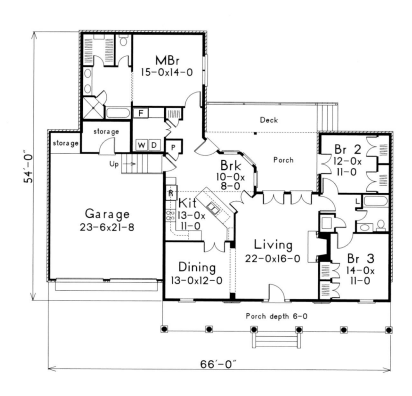

Full Pillared Porch Makes A Grand Entrance

1,800 total square feet of living area

Special features
- Energy efficient home with 2" x 6" exterior walls
- The stylish kitchen and breakfast area feature large windows that allow a great view outdoors
- Covered front and rear porches provide an added dimension to this home's living space
- Generous storage areas and a large utility room
- Large separate master bedroom with adjoining bath has a large tub and corner shower
- 3 bedrooms, 2 baths, 2-car garage
- Crawl space foundation, drawings also include slab foundation

Price Code C

Lockwood

Prestige Abounds In A Classic Ranch

2,723 total square feet of living area

Special features

◆ A large porch invites you into an elegant foyer which accesses a vaulted study with private hall and coat closet

◆ Great room is second to none, comprised of a fireplace, built-in shelves, vaulted ceiling and a 1 1/2 story window wall

◆ A spectacular hearth room with vaulted ceiling and masonry fireplace opens to an elaborate kitchen featuring two snack bars, a cooking island and walk-in pantry

◆ 4 bedrooms, 2 1/2 baths, 3-car side entry garage

◆ Basement foundation

Price Code E

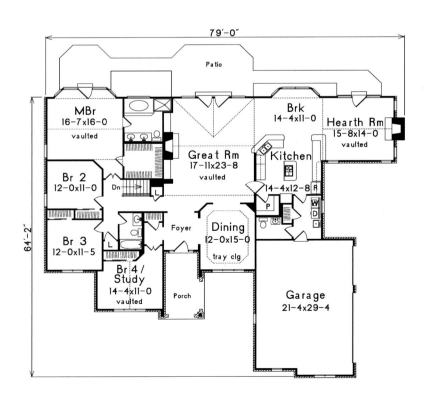

To order this plan, visit the Menards Building Materials Desk.

Dorset

Open Living Area Adds Drama

1,340 total square feet of living area

Special features

◆ Master bedroom has a private bath and walk-in closet
◆ Recessed entry leads to the vaulted family room that shares a see-through fireplace with the kitchen/dining area
◆ Garage includes a handy storage area
◆ Convenient laundry closet is located in the kitchen
◆ 3 bedrooms, 2 baths, 2-car side entry garage
◆ Slab foundation, drawings also include crawl space foundation

Price Code A

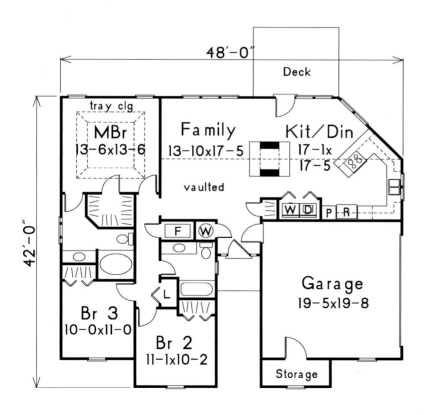

48'-0"

Deck

tray clg

MBr
13-6x13-6

Family
13-10x17-5

Kit/Din
17-1x
17-5

vaulted

42'-0"

W D   P R

F   W

Br 3
10-0x11-0

L

Garage
19-5x19-8

Br 2
11-1x10-2

Storage

Elmsdale

Sweeping Ranch With Hip Roof

1,315 total square feet of living area

Special features

◆ Dining room has a sliding door to the rear patio
◆ Large storage space in garage
◆ Cozy eating area in the kitchen
◆ Kitchen has easy access to the laundry/mud room
◆ Large living room with double closets for storage and coats
◆ 3 bedrooms, 2 baths, 2-car garage
◆ Basement foundation, drawings also include slab foundation

Price Code B

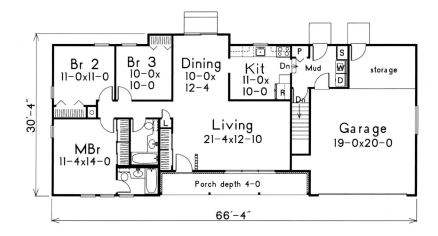

To order this plan, visit the Menards Building Materials Desk.

Delta Queen I

Inviting Front Porch

1,285 total square feet of living area

Special features

- ◆ Energy efficient home with 2" x 6" exterior walls
- ◆ Master bedroom includes a dressing area, private bath and built-in bookcase
- ◆ Kitchen features pantry, breakfast bar and complete view to the dining room
- ◆ Large storage area at the rear of the house
- ◆ 3 bedrooms, 2 baths
- ◆ Crawl space foundation, drawings also include basement and slab foundations

Price Code B

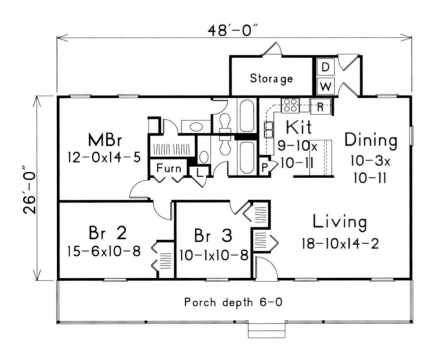

48´-0˝

26´-0˝

Storage

D
W
R

MBr
12-0x14-5

Furn   L

Kit
9-10x
10-11

P

Dining
10-3x
10-11

Br 2
15-6x10-8

Br 3
10-1x10-8

Living
18-10x14-2

Porch depth 6-0

Wilshire

Efficient And Attractive

2,076 total square feet of living area

Special features

◆ Energy efficient home with 2" x 6" exterior walls

◆ Superbly designed kitchen will make food preparation a breeze

◆ Family room and patio are perfectly located for side yard oriented views

◆ Large living and dining rooms capitalize on rear views while still convenient to entry

◆ A compartmented bath and good-sized walk-in closet adjoin the master bedroom

◆ 4 bedrooms, 2 baths, 2-car side entry garage

◆ Partial basement/crawl space foundation, drawings also include crawl space foundation

Price Code C

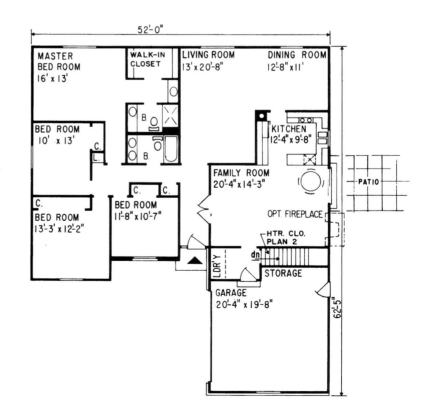

To order this plan, visit the Menards Building Materials Desk.

Wydown

Spacious And Open Family Living Area

1,416 total square feet of living area

Special features

◆ Family room includes fireplace, elevated plant shelf and vaulted ceiling
◆ Patio is accessible from the dining area and garage
◆ Centrally located laundry area
◆ Oversized walk-in pantry in the kitchen
◆ 3 bedrooms, 2 baths, 2-car garage
◆ Basement foundation, drawings also include crawl space and slab foundations

Price Code A

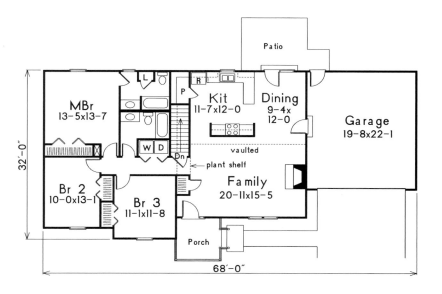

Florence

Comfortable One-Story Country Home

1,367 total square feet of living area

Special features

- ◆ Energy efficient home with 2" x 6" exterior walls
- ◆ Neat front porch shelters the entrance
- ◆ Dining room has a full wall of windows and storage area
- ◆ Breakfast area leads to the rear terrace through sliding doors
- ◆ The large living room features a high ceiling, skylight and fireplace
- ◆ 3 bedrooms, 2 baths, 2-car garage
- ◆ Basement foundation, drawings also include slab foundation

Price Code B

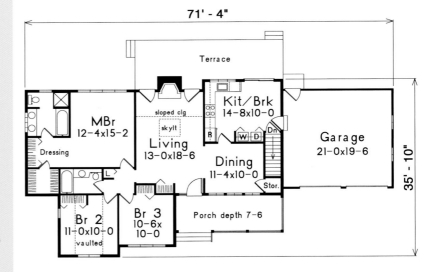

To order this plan, visit the Menards Building Materials Desk.

Plan #M01-007D-0002

MENARDS

Rear View

Clayton

Ultimate Atrium
For A Sloping Lot

3,814 total square feet of living area

Special features

- ◆ Massive sunken great room with vaulted ceiling includes exciting balcony overlook of towering atrium window wall
- ◆ Breakfast bar adjoins open "California" kitchen
- ◆ Seven vaulted rooms for drama and four fireplaces for warmth
- ◆ Master bath is complemented by the colonnade and fireplace surrounding the sunken tub and deck
- ◆ 3 bedrooms, 2 1/2 baths, 3-car side entry garage
- ◆ Walk-out basement foundation
- ◆ 3,566 square feet on the first floor and 248 square feet on the lower level atrium

Price Code G

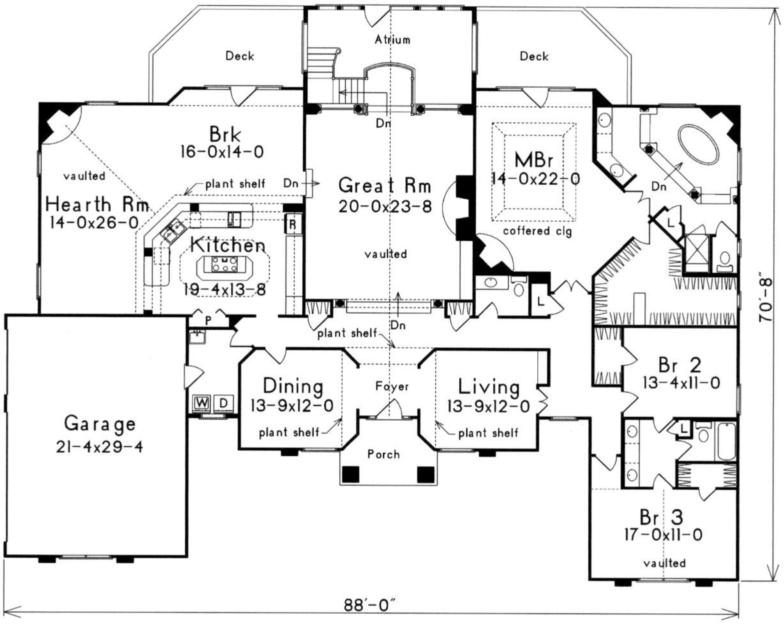

To order this plan, visit the Menards Building Materials Desk.

Floor plan labels:
- Deck
- Atrium
- Deck
- Brk 16-0x14-0
- vaulted
- plant shelf
- Dn
- Hearth Rm. 14-0x26-0
- Great Rm 20-0x23-8
- MBr 14-0x22-0
- Dn
- coffered clg
- Kitchen 19-4x13-8
- vaulted
- plant shelf
- Dn
- Garage 21-4x29-4
- WD
- Dining 13-9x12-0
- plant shelf
- Foyer
- Living 13-9x12-0
- plant shelf
- Br 2 13-4x11-0
- Porch
- Br 3 17-0x11-0
- vaulted
- 70'-8"
- 88'-0"

Stafford

Casual Exterior, Filled With Great Features

1,958 total square feet of living area

Special features

◆ Large wrap-around kitchen opens to a bright and cheerful breakfast area with access to large covered deck and open stairway to basement
◆ Kitchen is nestled between the dining and breakfast rooms
◆ Master bedroom includes a large walk-in closet, double-bowl vanity, garden tub and separate shower
◆ Foyer features an attractive plant shelf and opens into the living room that includes a lovely central fireplace
◆ 3 bedrooms, 2 baths, 2-car garage
◆ Basement foundation

Price Code C

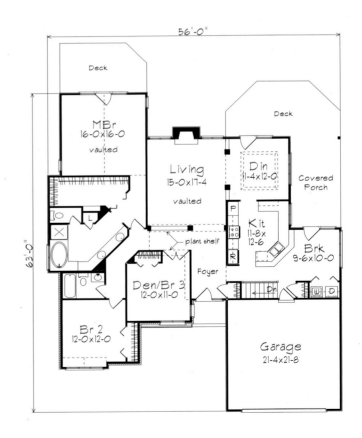

To order this plan, visit the Menards Building Materials Desk.

Lindenwood

Comfortable Family Living In This Ranch

1,994 total square feet of living area

Special features
- Convenient entrance from the garage into the main living area through the utility room
- Bedroom #2 features a 12' vaulted ceiling and the dining room boasts a 10' ceiling
- Master bedroom offers a full bath with an oversized tub, separate shower and walk-in closet
- Entry leads to the formal dining room and attractive living room with double French doors and fireplace
- 3 bedrooms, 2 baths, 2-car garage
- Slab foundation

Price Code D

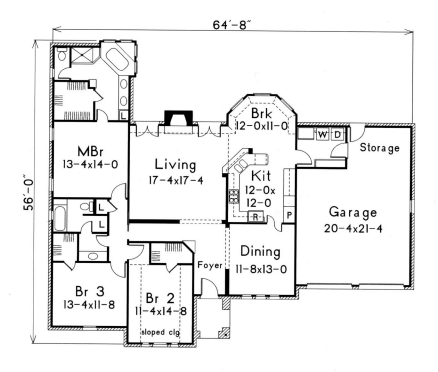

To order this plan, visit the Menards Building Materials Desk.

Bellevue

Attractive And Spacious Brick Ranch

1,778 total square feet of living area

Special features

- ◆ Formal entryway leads into the large living room
- ◆ Family room with fireplace opens to the patio
- ◆ Designed for practicality, the kitchen and dining area are adjacent to the mud room/lavatory area that opens to the garage
- ◆ Designed to allow an additional bedroom if future expansion is desired
- ◆ Future fourth bedroom has an additional 266 square feet of living area
- ◆ 3 bedrooms, 2 1/2 baths, 2-car garage
- ◆ Basement foundation, drawings also include crawl space foundation

Price Code B

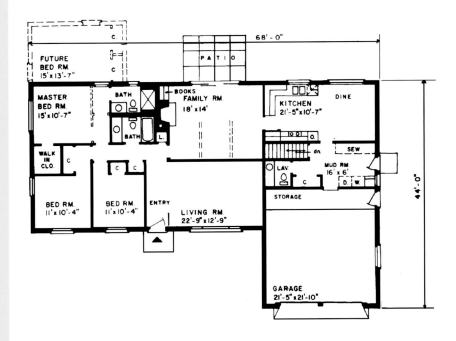

To order this plan, visit the Menards Building Materials Desk.

Plan #M01-007D-0135

MENARDS

Summerplace

Two Bedroom Cottage With Garage And Shop

801 total square feet of living area

Special features

◆ A wrap-around porch, roof dormer and fancy stonework all contribute to a delightful and charming exterior

◆ The living room enjoys a separate entry, a stone fireplace, vaulted ceiling and lots of windows

◆ The well-equipped kitchen has a snack bar and dining area with bay which offers access to the rear patio

◆ An oversized two-car garage features a large vaulted room ideal for a shop, studio, hobby room or office with built-in cabinets and access to the porch

◆ 2 bedrooms, 1 bath, 2-car side entry garage

◆ Slab foundation

Price Code AAA

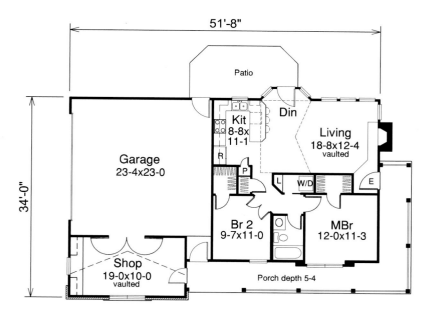

To order this plan, visit the Menards Building Materials Desk.

Taylor

Half-Round Highlights And Gables Unify The Facade

1,847 total square feet of living area

Special features
◆ Kitchen includes an island cooktop and sunny breakfast area
◆ Master bedroom features a vaulted ceiling and a skylighted bath with large tub, separate shower and walk-in closet
◆ Service bar eases entertaining in the vaulted dining and living rooms
◆ Family room, complete with corner fireplace, accesses outdoor patio
◆ 3 bedrooms, 2 baths, 2-car garage
◆ Slab foundation

Price Code C

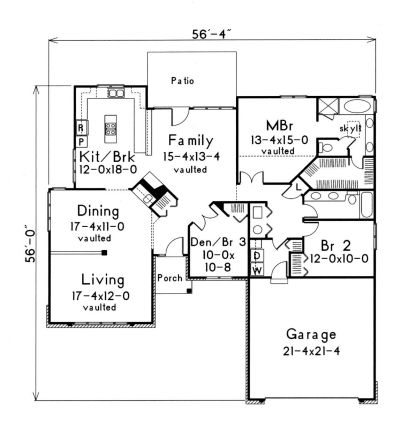

To order this plan, visit the Menards Building Materials Desk.

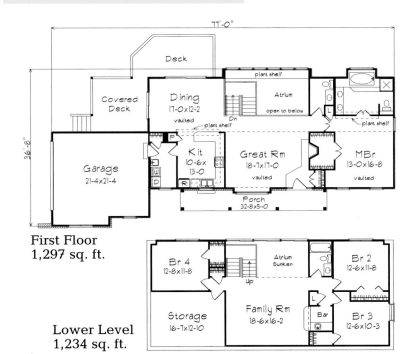

Rear View

Southton

Traditional Exterior Boasts Exciting Interior

2,531 total square feet of living area

Special features

◆ Charming porch with dormers leads into the vaulted great room with atrium
◆ Well-designed kitchen and breakfast bar adjoin an extra-large laundry/mud room
◆ Double sinks, tub with window above and plant shelf complete the vaulted master bath
◆ 4 bedrooms, 2 1/2 baths, 2-car side entry garage
◆ Walk-out basement foundation

Price Code D

First Floor 1,297 sq. ft.

Lower Level 1,234 sq. ft.

To order this plan, visit the Menards Building Materials Desk.

Royal Oak

Ideal For A Shallow Lot

1,414 total square feet of living area

Special features
- Energy efficient home with 2" x 6" exterior walls
- Charming U-shaped kitchen offers lots of space with adjacent dining area
- Convenient to kitchen is a spacious laundry room and stairs to the basement
- Spacious living room with ample closet space
- 3 bedrooms, 2 baths, 2-car garage
- Basement foundation, drawings also include crawl space and slab foundations

Price Code A

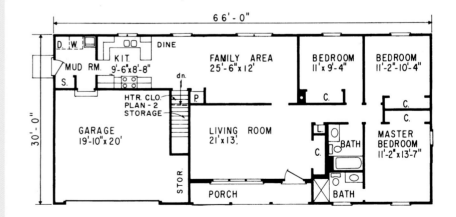

66' - 0"

30' - 0"

D. W.

DINE

MUD RM.

KIT. 9'-6"x 8'-8"

S.

FAMILY AREA 25'-6"x 12'

BEDROOM 11' x 9'-4"

BEDROOM 11'-2"-10'-4"

HTR. CLO. PLAN - 2 STORAGE

dn.

P

C.

C.

GARAGE 19'-10"x 20'

LIVING ROOM 21'x 13'

BATH

C.

C.

MASTER BEDROOM 11'-2"x13'-7"

STOR.

PORCH

BATH

To order this plan, visit the Menards Building Materials Desk.

Old Hickory

Split-Level Design Ultimate In Convenience

1,056 total square feet of living area

Special features

◆ L-shaped kitchen with adjoining dining area
◆ Large unfinished basement ideal for future living space
◆ Side entrance into dining and living areas
◆ All bedrooms located on upper level for privacy
◆ 3 bedrooms, 1 1/2 baths
◆ Partial basement/crawl space foundation

Price Code AA

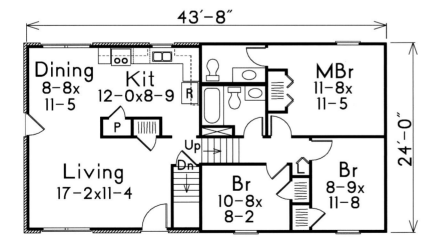

43'-8"

24'-0"

Dining
8-8x
11-5

Kit
12-0x8-9

MBr
11-8x
11-5

Living
17-2x11-4

Up

Dn

Br
10-8x
8-2

Br
8-9x
11-8

P

R

Seville

Facade Combines Siding And Brick With Arch Window

2,159 total square feet of living area

Special features
◆ Energy efficient home with 2" x 6" exterior walls
◆ Covered entry opens into the large foyer with a skylight and coat closet
◆ Master bedroom includes a private bath with angled vanity, separate spa and shower and walk-in closet
◆ Family and living rooms feature vaulted ceilings and sunken floors for added openness
◆ Kitchen features an island counter and convenient pantry
◆ 3 bedrooms, 2 baths, 2-car garage
◆ Basement foundation, drawings also include crawl space and slab foundations

Price Code C

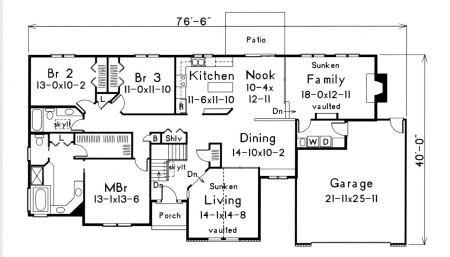

104

To order this plan, visit the Menards Building Materials Desk.

Riverview

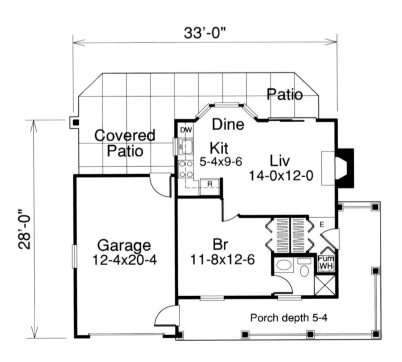

Cozy Retreat For Weekends

480 total square feet of living area

Special features
◆ Inviting wrap-around porch and rear covered patio are perfect for summer evenings
◆ Living room features a fireplace, separate entry foyer with coat closet and sliding doors to rear patio
◆ The compact but complete kitchen includes a dining area with bay window and window at sink for patio views
◆ 1 bedroom, 1 bath, 1-car garage
◆ Slab foundation

Price Code AAA

To order this plan, visit the Menards Building Materials Desk.

Laurel

Upscale Ranch Boasts Both Formal And Casual Areas

1,950 total square feet of living area

Special features

- ◆ Large corner kitchen with island cooktop opens to the family room
- ◆ Master bedroom features a double-door entry, raised ceiling, double-bowl vanity and walk-in closet
- ◆ Plant shelf accents hall
- ◆ 4 bedrooms, 2 baths, 3-car garage
- ◆ Crawl space foundation

Price Code C

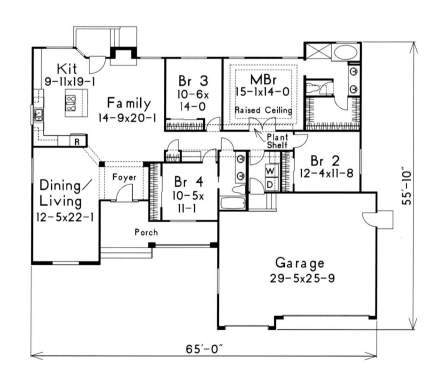

Shadyview

Country Ranch Enjoys Large Great Room

1,944 total square feet of living area

Special features

- Spacious surrounding porch, covered patio and stone fireplace create an expansive ponderosa appearance
- The large entry leads to a grand-sized great room featuring a vaulted ceiling, fireplace, wet bar and access to the porch through three patio doors
- The U-shaped kitchen is open to the hearth room and enjoys a snack bar, fireplace and patio access
- A luxury bath, walk-in closet and doors to the porch are a few of the amenities of the master bedroom
- 3 bedrooms, 2 baths, 3-car detached garage
- Basement foundation

Price Code C

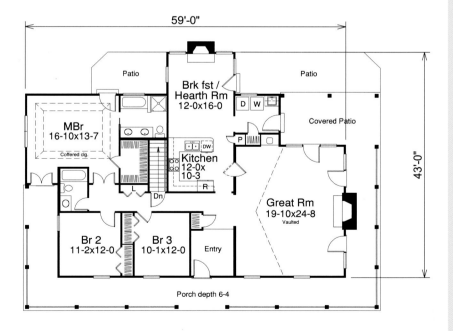

59'-0"

Patio

Brk fst / Hearth Rm
12-0x16-0

Patio

D W

Covered Patio

MBr
16-10x13-7

Coffered clg.

P

Kitchen
12-0x
10-3

DW

L

Dn

R

43'-0"

Great Rm
19-10x24-8
Vaulted

Br 2
11-2x12-0

Br 3
10-1x12-0

Entry

Porch depth 6-4

Ava

Rustic Stone Exterior

1,466 total square feet of living area

Special features

- ◆ Energy efficient home with 2" x 6" exterior walls
- ◆ Foyer separates the living room from the dining room and contains a generous coat closet
- ◆ Large living room features a corner fireplace, bay window and pass-through to the kitchen
- ◆ Informal breakfast area opens to a large terrace through sliding glass doors which brighten the area
- ◆ Master bedroom has a large walk-in closet and private bath
- ◆ 3 bedrooms, 2 baths, 2-car garage
- ◆ Basement foundation, drawings also include slab foundation

Price Code B

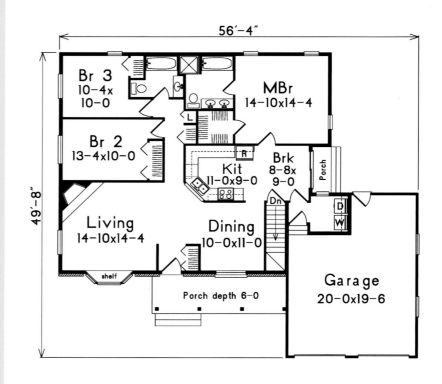

To order this plan, visit the Menards Building Materials Desk.

Hillbriar

Distinctive Home For Sloping Terrain

1,340 total square feet of living area

Special features

◆ Grand-sized vaulted living and dining rooms offer fireplace, wet bar and breakfast counter open to a spacious kitchen
◆ Vaulted master bedroom features a double-door entry, walk-in closet and an elegant bath
◆ Basement includes a huge two-car garage and space for a bedroom/bath expansion
◆ 3 bedrooms, 2 baths, 2-car drive under garage with storage area
◆ Basement foundation

Price Code A

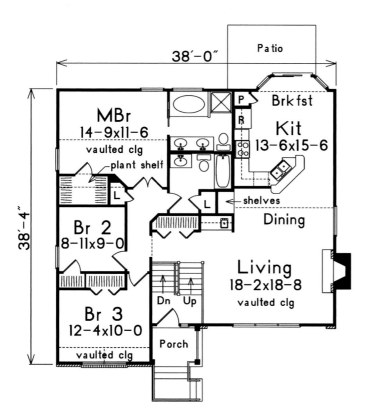

To order this plan, visit the Menards Building Materials Desk.

Sanibel

Family Room Features Barrel Vaulted Ceiling

2,153 total square feet of living area

Special features

◆ Foyer leads directly into the formal living room which accesses the porch

◆ Master bedroom features a wall of windows and also accesses the porch

◆ Family room boasts a 12' barrel vaulted ceiling and built-in bookshelves on each side of the dramatic fireplace

◆ Varied ceiling heights throughout

◆ Three bedrooms, a bath and the utility room are located off the family room

◆ 4 bedrooms, 2 baths, 2-car garage

◆ Slab foundation

Price Code C

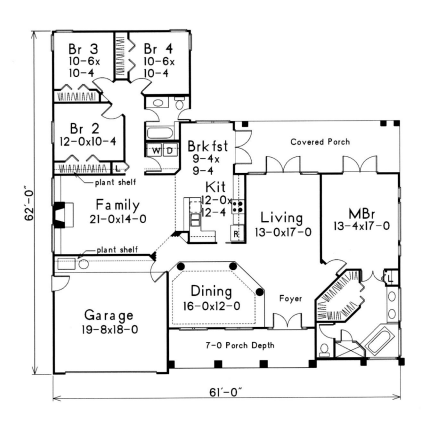

To order this plan, visit the Menards Building Materials Desk.

Foxton

Energy Efficient Ranch

1,176 total square feet of living area

Special features

- ◆ The living room features an entry area with large coat closet and box-bay window
- ◆ The kitchen has an eating area and adjoins a very spacious family area
- ◆ Master bedroom has a huge walk-in closet and shares a compartmented bath with two secondary bedrooms
- ◆ 3 bedrooms, 1 1/2 baths, 2-car optional garage
- ◆ Basement foundation, drawings also include crawl space and slab foundations

Price Code AA

42'-0" **22'-0"**

28'-0"

MASTER BEDROOM
12'x11'-2"

FAMILY AREA
12'-6"x13'-6"

KITCHEN
11'x10'

OPTIONAL GARAGE
21'-8"x23'-4"

dn

BEDROOM
11'-4"x10'-3"

BEDROOM
9'-4"x10'-3"

LIVING ROOM
15'x13'-8"

c.

To order this plan, visit the Menards Building Materials Desk.

Crawford

Roomy Ranch
For Easy Living

1,343 total square feet of living area

Special features
- Separate and convenient family, living and dining areas
- Nice-sized master bedroom enjoys a large closet and private bath
- Foyer with convenient coat closet opens into combined living and dining rooms
- Family room has access to the outdoors through sliding glass doors
- 3 bedrooms, 2 baths, 2-car garage
- Crawl space foundation, drawings also include basement foundation

Price Code A

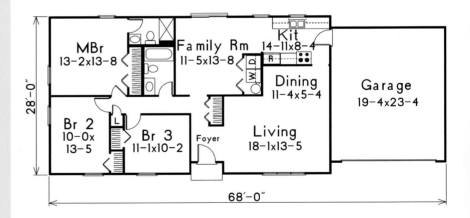

Alternate Stair Location

To order this plan, visit the Menards Building Materials Desk.

Sunbrook

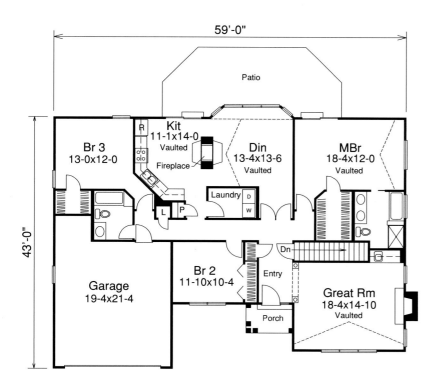

59'-0"

43'-0"

Patio

Br 3
13-0x12-0

Kit
11-1x14-0
Vaulted

Fireplace

Din
13-4x13-6
Vaulted

MBr
18-4x12-0
Vaulted

Laundry

Garage
19-4x21-4

Br 2
11-10x10-4

Entry

Dn

Great Rm
18-4x14-10
Vaulted

Porch

A Unique Place To Call Home

1,826 total square feet of living area

Special features
- An arched opening with columns invites you into a beautiful great room with fireplace, wet bar and vaulted ceiling
- A double-door entry leads into a large vaulted dining room with a fireplace, plant shelves and great view of the rear patio through a sweeping bay window
- Every bedroom enjoys private zoning with lots of closet space
- 3 bedrooms, 2 baths, 2-car garage
- Basement foundation

Price Code C

MENARDS

Jamieson

Handsome Facade, Spacious Living Arrangement

2,396 total square feet of living area

Special features

◆ Energy efficient home with 2" x 6" exterior walls
◆ Generously wide entry welcomes guests
◆ Central living area with a 12' ceiling and large fireplace serves as a convenient traffic hub
◆ Kitchen is secluded, yet has easy access to the living, dining and breakfast areas
◆ Deluxe master bath has a walk-in closet, oversized tub, shower and other amenities
◆ 4 bedrooms, 2 baths, 2-car garage
◆ Slab foundation, drawings also include basement and crawl space foundations

Price Code D

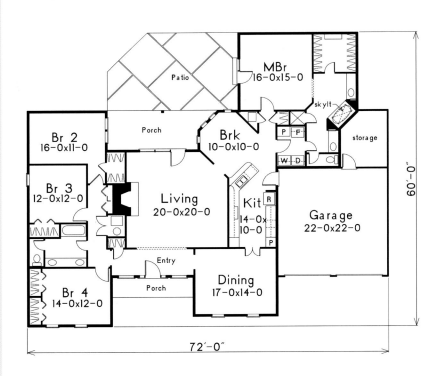

To order this plan, visit the Menards Building Materials Desk.

Plan #M01-027D-0003

MENARDS

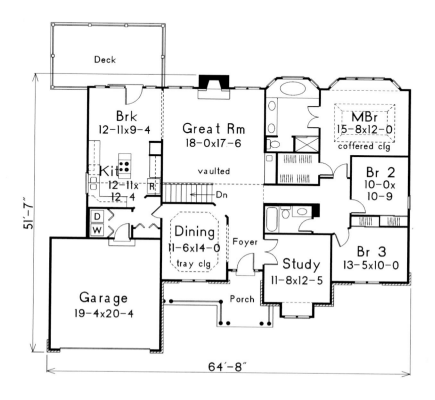

Questover

Classic Three Bedroom

2,061 total square feet of living area

Special features

- ◆ Convenient entrance from garage into home through laundry room
- ◆ Master bedroom features a walk-in closet and double-door entrance into master bath with an oversized tub
- ◆ Formal dining room enjoys a tray ceiling
- ◆ Kitchen features island cooktop and adjacent breakfast room
- ◆ 3 bedrooms, 2 baths, 2-car garage
- ◆ Basement foundation

Price Code D

To order this plan, visit the Menards Building Materials Desk.

115

Whitefield

Unique Sectioning For Entertaining

1,593 total square feet of living area

Special features

- ◆ A welcoming porch invites you into a spacious living room
- ◆ Kitchen and dining room is open to family room through wood balustrade
- ◆ Master bedroom offers private bath and two closets
- ◆ Laundry/mud room located directly off garage with convenient access to the outdoors
- ◆ 3 bedrooms, 2 baths, 2-car garage
- ◆ Basement foundation, drawings also include crawl space and slab foundations

Price Code B

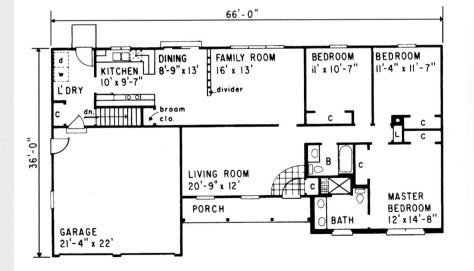

66'-0"

36'-0"

d
w
L'DRY
c
dn.

KITCHEN
10' x 9'-7"

DINING
8'-9" x 13'

FAMILY ROOM
16' x 13'
divider

BEDROOM
11' x 10'-7"

BEDROOM
11'-4" x 11'-7"

c

c

broom
clo.

L
c
c

B
c

c

LIVING ROOM
20'-9" x 12'

PORCH

BATH

MASTER
BEDROOM
12' x14'-8"

GARAGE
21'-4" x 22'

Santa Jenita

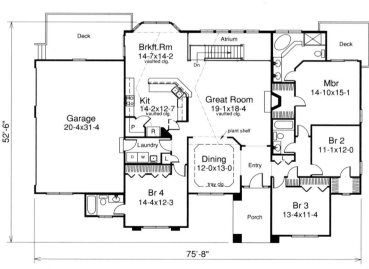

Deck

Brkft.Rm
14-7x14-2
vaulted clg.

Atrium

Dn

Deck

Kit
14-2x12-7
vaulted clg.

Great Room
19-1x18-4
vaulted clg.

Mbr
14-10x15-1

Garage
20-4x31-4

P

R

Laundry

D W L

plant shelf

Br 2
11-1x12-0

52'-6"

Dining
12-0x13-0
tray clg

Entry

Br 4
14-4x12-3

Br 3
13-4x11-4

Porch

75'-8"

First Floor
2,408 sq. ft.

Up

Sitting Rm
12-6x7-4

Family Rm
19-1x18-4

Office/ Br 5
14-1x17-6

**Optional
Lower Level**

Basement

Floridian Architecture With Mother-In-Law Suite

2,408 total square feet of living area

Special features

◆ Large vaulted great room overlooks atrium and window wall, adjoins dining room, spacious breakfast room with bay and pass-through kitchen

◆ A special private bedroom with bath, separate from other bedrooms, is perfect for a mother-in-law suite or children home from college

◆ Atrium opens to 1,100 square feet of optional living area below

◆ 4 bedrooms, 3 baths, 3-car side entry garage

◆ Walk-out basement foundation

Price Code D

To order this plan, visit the Menards Building Materials Desk.

Countryside

Affordable, Upscale And Amenity-Full

1,643 total square feet of living area

Special features

◆ Family room has a vaulted ceiling, open staircase and arched windows allowing for plenty of light

◆ Kitchen captures full use of space, with a pantry, storage, ample counterspace and work island

◆ Large closets and storage areas throughout

◆ Roomy master bath has a skylight for natural lighting plus a separate tub and shower

◆ Rear of house provides ideal location for future screened-in porch

◆ 3 bedrooms, 2 baths, 2-car side entry garage

◆ Basement foundation, drawings also include slab and crawl space foundations

Price Code B

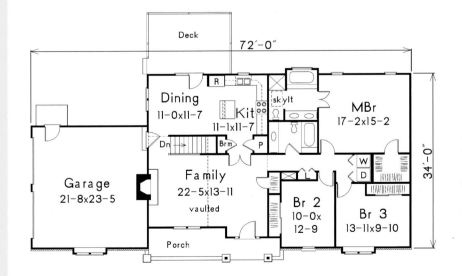

To order this plan, visit the Menards Building Materials Desk.

Ellisville

Single Level Traditional

3,412 total square feet of living area

Special features

◆ Large formal dining room with vaulted ceiling is adjacent to the entry foyer
◆ Expansive great room boasts a dramatic fireplace and vaulted ceiling
◆ Master bedroom and library are secluded from other living areas
◆ Family-style kitchen includes pantry, island cooktop and large breakfast area
◆ Sunken master bedroom has patio access and a luxurious private bath
◆ 3 bedrooms, 3 1/2 baths, 2-car side entry garage
◆ Basement foundation

Price Code F

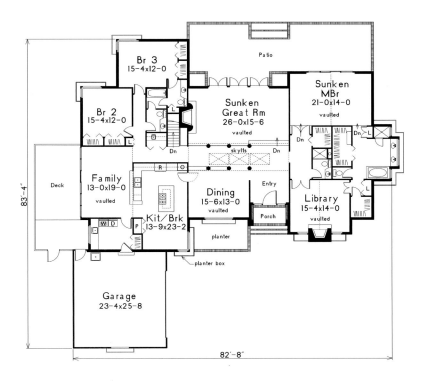

To order this plan, visit the Menards Building Materials Desk.

Summerpark

Bright And Airy Country Design

1,591 total square feet of living area

Special features

◆ Spacious porch and patio provide outdoor enjoyment

◆ Large entry foyer leads to a cheery kitchen and breakfast room which welcomes the sun through a wide array of windows

◆ The great room features a vaulted ceiling, corner fireplace, wet bar and access to the rear patio

◆ Double walk-in closets, private porch and a luxury bath are special highlights of the vaulted master bedroom suite

◆ 3 bedrooms, 2 baths, 2-car side entry garage

◆ Basement foundation

Price Code B

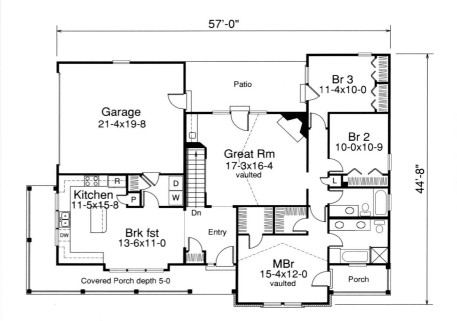

To order this plan, visit the Menards Building Materials Desk.

Fontana

Contemporary Excellence

2,180 total square feet of living area

Special features

◆ Large impressive entry for receiving guests
◆ Activity and dining rooms have vaulted ceilings, fireplace, wet bar and expansive bay windows which are second to none
◆ Master bedroom and bath have been designed on a grand scale
◆ All bedrooms feature vaulted ceilings and spacious closets
◆ 3 bedrooms, 2 baths, 2-car garage
◆ Partial basement/crawl space foundation, drawings also include partial slab/crawl space foundation

Price Code C

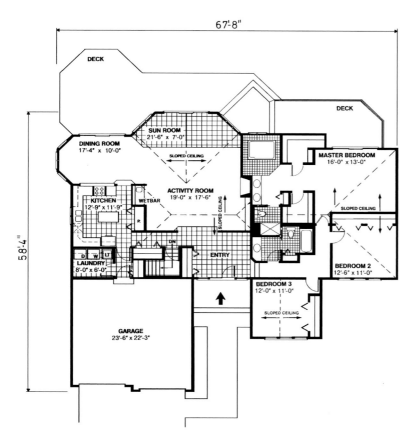

To order this plan, visit the Menards Building Materials Desk.

Stratton

High-Style Vaulted Ranch

1,453 total square feet of living area

Special features

◆ Decorative vents, window trim, shutters and brick blend to create dramatic curb appeal

◆ Energy efficient home with 2" x 6" exterior walls

◆ Kitchen opens to the living area and includes a salad sink in the island as well as a pantry and handy laundry room

◆ Exquisite master bedroom is highlighted by a vaulted ceiling, dressing area with walk-in closet, private bath and spa tub/shower

◆ 3 bedrooms, 2 baths, 2-car garage

◆ Basement foundation, drawings also include crawl space foundation

Price Code A

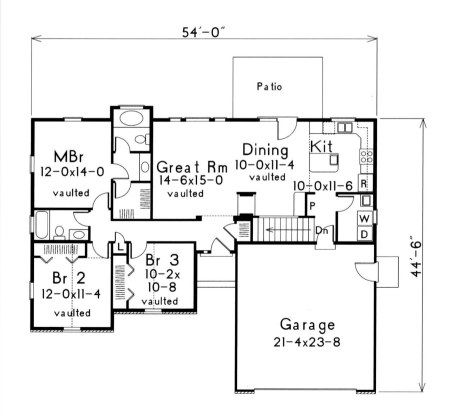

To order this plan, visit the Menards Building Materials Desk.

MENARDS

LaFayette

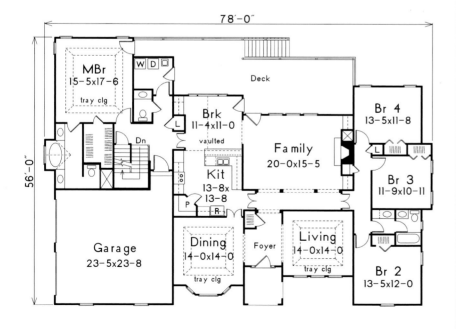

Striking Front Facade With Arched Entry

2,718 total square feet of living area

Special features

◆ Master bedroom has a tray ceiling, access to the rear deck, walk-in closet and an impressive private bath

◆ Dining and living rooms flank the foyer and both feature tray ceilings

◆ Spacious family room features a 12' ceiling, fireplace and access to the rear deck

◆ Kitchen has a 9' ceiling, large pantry and bar overlooking the breakfast room

◆ 4 bedrooms, 2 1/2 baths, 2-car side entry garage

◆ Basement foundation

Price Code E

Madison Manor

Country Home Focused On Patio Views

2,547 total square feet of living area

Special features

◆ Grand-sized great room features a 12' volume ceiling, fireplace with built-in wrap-around shelving and patio doors with sidelights and transom windows

◆ The walk-in pantry, computer desk, large breakfast island for seven and bayed breakfast area are the many features of this outstanding kitchen

◆ The master bedroom suite enjoys a luxurious bath, large walk-in closets and patio access

◆ 4 bedrooms, 2 1/2 baths, 3-car side entry garage

◆ Basement foundation

Price Code D

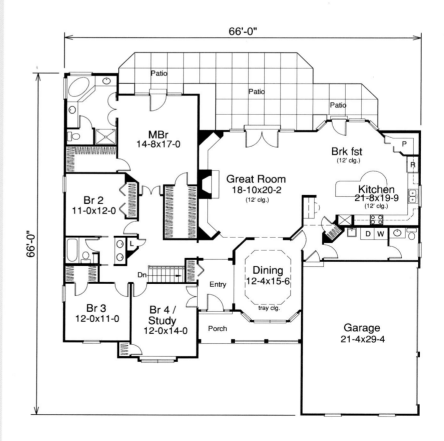

124

Woodbury

Quaint Cottage With Inviting Front Porch

1,020 total square feet of living area

Special features
- Living room is warmed by a fireplace
- Dining and living rooms are enhanced by vaulted ceilings and plant shelves
- U-shaped kitchen features a large window over the sink
- 2 bedrooms, 1 bath
- Slab foundation

Price Code AA

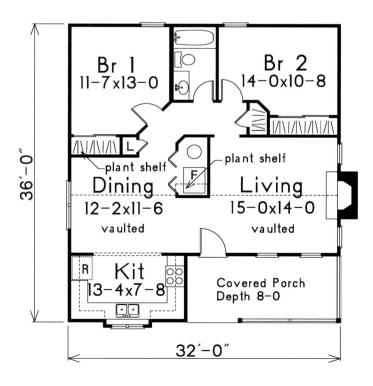

To order this plan, visit the Menards Building Materials Desk.

Wrenwood

Bold Windows Enhance Front Entry

2,252 total square feet of living area

Special features

- Energy efficient home with 2" x 6" exterior walls
- Central living area
- Private master bedroom features a large walk-in closet, dressing area and bath
- Secondary bedrooms are in a suite arrangement with plenty of closet space
- Sunny breakfast room looks out over the porch and patio
- Large entry area is highlighted by circle-top transoms
- 4 bedrooms, 2 baths, 2-car garage
- Slab foundation, drawings also include basement and crawl space foundations

Price Code D

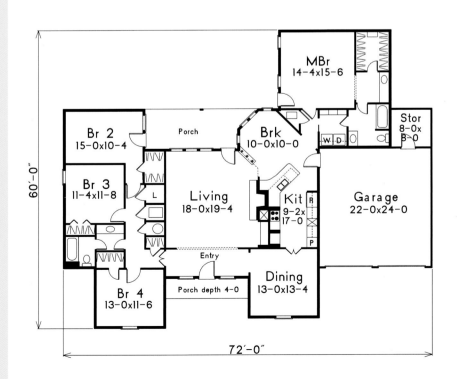

To order this plan, visit the Menards Building Materials Desk.

Inverness I

Beauty And Practicality Designed As One

1,504 total square feet of living area

Special features

◆ Private master bedroom features double walk-in closets, linen closet and bath
◆ Laundry room is conveniently located near garage
◆ Open great room and dining area create a spacious living atmosphere
◆ Generous closet space in secondary bedrooms
◆ Kitchen features breakfast bar, pantry and storage closet
◆ 3 bedrooms, 2 baths, 2-car garage
◆ Crawl space foundation, drawings also include basement and slab foundations

Price Code B

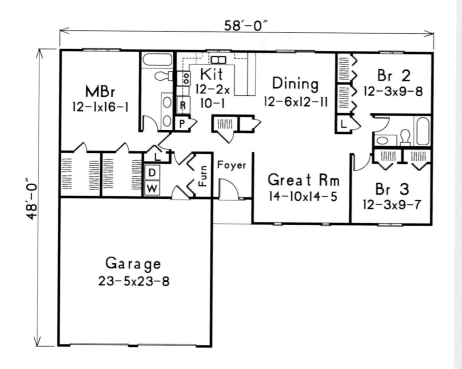

58'-0"

48'-0"

MBr
12-1x16-1

Kit
12-2x
10-1

Dining
12-6x12-11

Br 2
12-3x9-8

Foyer

Furn

Great Rm
14-10x14-5

Br 3
12-3x9-7

Garage
23-5x23-8

To order this plan, visit the Menards Building Materials Desk.

127

Plan #M01-048D-0009

MENARDS

Bellerive

Soaring Covered Portico

2,056 total square feet of living area

Special features

- Columned foyer projects past the living and dining rooms into the family room
- Kitchen conveniently accesses the dining room and breakfast area
- Master bedroom features double-door access to the patio and a pocket door to the private bath with walk-in closet, double-bowl vanity and tub
- 4 bedrooms, 2 baths, 2-car garage
- Slab foundation, drawings also include crawl space foundation

Price Code C

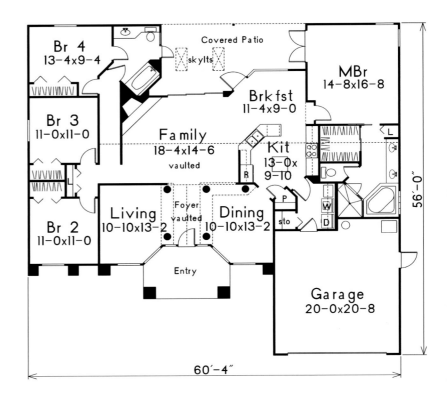

To order this plan, visit the Menards Building Materials Desk.

Pineridge

Popular Country Haven

1,248 total square feet of living area

Special features

◆ Harmonious design of stonework and gables create the perfect country retreat
◆ Large country porch is ideal for relaxing on evenings
◆ Great room and dining area enjoy a vaulted ceiling, corner fireplace and views of rear patio through two sets of sliding doors
◆ Large walk-in pantry, U-shaped cabinetry and pass-through snack bar are a few features of the smartly designed kitchen
◆ 2 bedrooms, 1 1/2 baths, 2-car side entry garage
◆ Basement foundation, drawings also include slab foundation

Price Code A

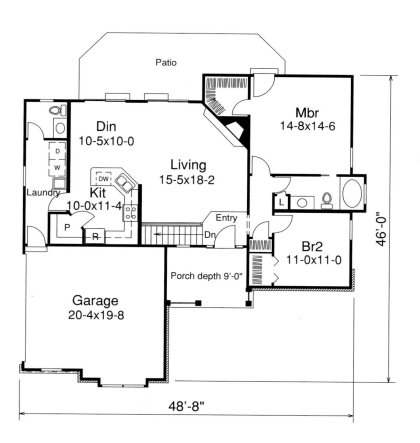

Patio

Din
10-5x10-0

Mbr
14-8x14-6

Living
15-5x18-2

Laundry

Kit
10-0x11-4

Entry
Dn

L

Br2
11-0x11-0

P

R

Porch depth 9'-0"

Garage
20-4x19-8

46'-0"

48'-8"

To order this plan, visit the Menards Building Materials Desk.

Savannah

Double Gables
Frame Front Porch

1,832 total square feet of living area

Special features

◆ Distinctive master bedroom is enhanced by skylights, garden tub, separate shower and walk-in closet
◆ U-shaped kitchen features a convenient pantry, laundry area and full view to breakfast room
◆ Foyer opens into spacious living room
◆ Large front porch creates enjoyable outdoor living
◆ 2" x 6" exterior walls available, please order plan #M01-001D-0127
◆ 3 bedrooms, 2 baths, 2-car detached garage
◆ Crawl space foundation, drawings also include basement and slab foundations

Price Code C

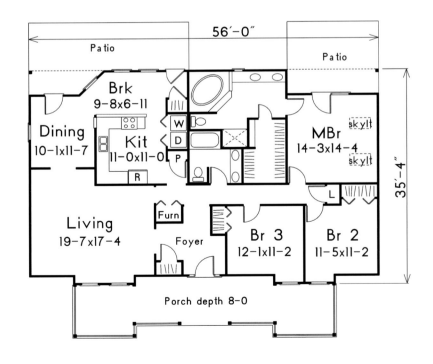

To order this plan, visit the Menards Building Materials Desk.

Finley

Open Living Area

1,993 total square feet of living area

Special features
- ◆ The airy family room enjoys the ease of organization with built-in shelves flanking the fireplace
- ◆ An eating bar and pantry add efficiency to the kitchen
- ◆ Split bedrooms ensure privacy
- ◆ 3 bedrooms, 2 baths, 2-car side entry garage
- ◆ Basement foundation

Price Code AA

To order this plan, visit the Menards Building Materials Desk.

Plan #M01-008D-0129

MENARDS

Belleair

Affordable And Spaciously Designed Ranch

1,288 total square feet of living area

Special features

- Large living room expands visually through bi-fold doors when third bedroom is utilized as a study
- Spacious eat-in kitchen adjoins sunny family room
- First floor laundry closet makes laundry easy
- Cheerful master bedroom has a private bath and shower
- 3 bedrooms, 2 baths, 2-car garage
- Basement foundation, drawings also include crawl space and slab foundations

Price Code A

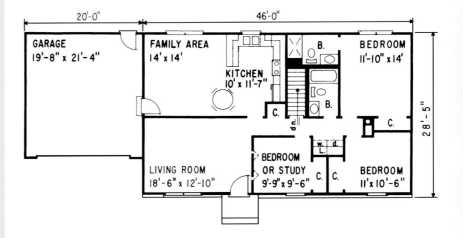

To order this plan, visit the Menards Building Materials Desk.

MENARDS

Country Manor

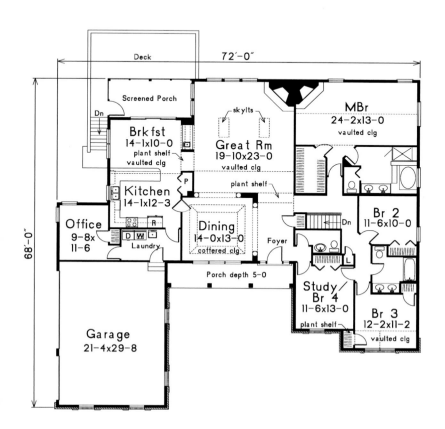

Deck

Screened Porch

72'-0"

Dn

Brk fst
14-1x10-0
plant shelf
vaulted clg

skylts

Great Rm
19-10x23-0
vaulted clg

MBr
24-2x13-0
vaulted clg

Kitchen
14-1x12-3

P

plant shelf

Office
9-8x
11-6

D W
Laundry

R

Dining
14-0x13-0
coffered clg

Foyer

Br 2
11-6x10-0

Dn

L

68'-0"

Porch depth 5-0

Study/
Br 4
11-6x13-0
plant shelf

Br 3
12-2x11-2
vaulted clg

Garage
21-4x29-8

705

Excellent Ranch For A Country Setting

2,758 total square feet of living area

Special features

- Energy efficient home with 2" x 6" exterior walls
- Vaulted great room excels with fireplace, wet bar, plant shelves and skylights
- Fabulous master bedroom enjoys a fireplace, large bath, walk-in closet and vaulted ceiling
- Trendsetting kitchen and breakfast area adjoins the spacious screened porch
- Convenient office near kitchen is perfect for a computer room, hobby enthusiast or fifth bedroom
- 4 bedrooms, 2 1/2 baths, 3-car side entry garage
- Basement foundation

Price Code E

To order this plan, visit the Menards Building Materials Desk.

Parkside

Exquisite Double-Door Entry

2,305 total square feet of living area

Special features

◆ Living room features a large window for outdoor views

◆ The left side of the home includes a master bedroom with spacious walk-in closet and the option of connecting to one of three remaining bedrooms for use as a den

◆ Family room with walk-out to patio is adjacent to a lovely dining room

◆ L-shaped counter in kitchen creates an open atmosphere when connected with the breakfast room

◆ 4 bedrooms 2 1/2 baths, 2-car side entry garage

◆ Partial basement/crawl space foundation, drawings also include slab foundation

Price Code D

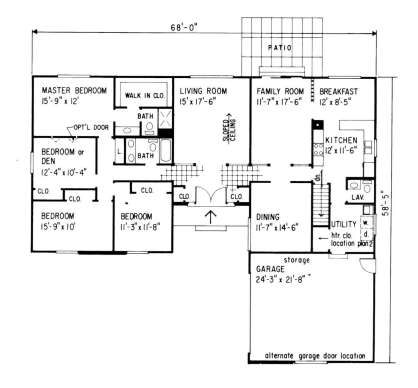

To order this plan, visit the Menards Building Materials Desk.

Aspen

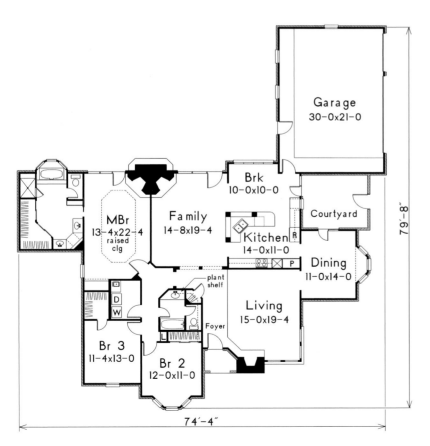

Fireplaces Are Unique Focal Points

2,481 total square feet of living area

Special features

◆ Varied ceiling heights throughout this home
◆ Master bedroom features a built-in desk and pocket-door entrance into the large master bath
◆ Master bath includes a corner vanity and garden tub
◆ Breakfast area accesses the courtyard
◆ 3 bedrooms, 2 baths, 3-car side entry garage
◆ Slab foundation

Price Code D

To order this plan, visit the Menards Building Materials Desk.

Freemont

Fully Columned Front Entrance

2,365 total square feet of living area

Special features

◆ 9' ceilings throughout the home
◆ Expansive central living room is complemented by a corner fireplace
◆ Breakfast bay overlooks the rear porch
◆ Master bedroom features a bath with two walk-in closets and vanities, separate tub and shower and handy linen closet
◆ Peninsula keeps kitchen private
◆ 4 bedrooms, 2 baths, 2-car carport
◆ Slab foundation

Price Code D

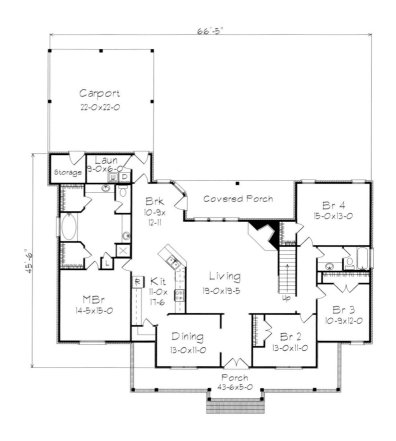

To order this plan, visit the Menards Building Materials Desk.

Stonegate Manor

Country Lodge With Screened Porch And Fireplace

1,568 total square feet of living area

Special features

◆ Multiple entrances from three porches help to bring the outdoors in

◆ The lodge-like great room features a vaulted ceiling, stone fireplace, step-up entrance foyer and opens to a huge screened porch

◆ The kitchen has an island and peninsula, a convenient laundry room and adjoins a spacious dining area which leads to a screened porch and rear patio

◆ The master bedroom has two walk-in closets, a luxury bath and access to the screened porch and patio

◆ 2 bedrooms, 2 baths, 3-car side entry garage

◆ Crawl space foundation

Price Code B

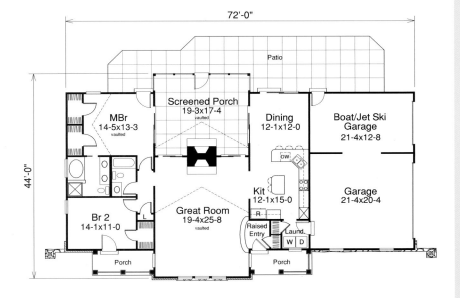

Rivermill

Gables Boost Attractive Facade

1,128 total square feet of living area

Special features

◆ Large living room borrows from dining area creating an expansive space

◆ Well-arranged U-shaped kitchen has lots of counter and cabinet storage space

◆ Double closets and a full bath accompany the spacious master bedroom

◆ Oversized garage with ample storage has a door to the rear patio that leads to the dining area

◆ 2 bedrooms, 2 baths, 2-car garage

◆ Basement foundation

Price Code AA

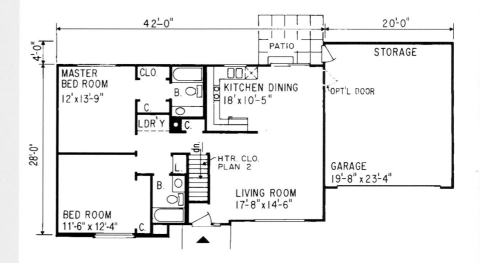

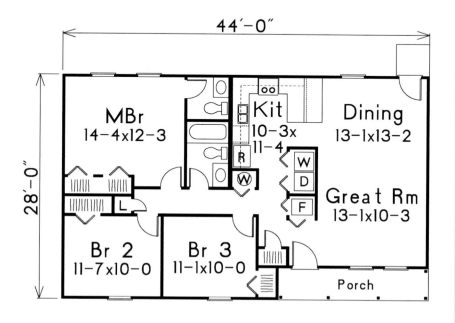

Pinehurst I

Large Great Room And Dining Area

1,160 total square feet of living area

Special features

- U-shaped kitchen includes breakfast bar and convenient laundry area
- Master bedroom features private half bath and large closet
- Dining room has outdoor access
- Dining and great rooms combine to create an open living atmosphere
- 3 bedrooms, 1 1/2 baths
- Crawl space foundation, drawings also include basement and slab foundations

Price Code AA

Floor plan dimensions:

44'-0" (width) × 28'-0" (depth)

- MBr 14-4x12-3
- Kit 10-3x11-4
- Dining 13-1x13-2
- Great Rm 13-1x10-3
- Br 2 11-7x10-0
- Br 3 11-1x10-0
- Porch

To order this plan, visit the Menards Building Materials Desk.

Summersville

High Styling Wraps Central Kitchen

3,003 total square feet of living area

Special features

- ◆ Energy efficient home with 2" x 6" exterior walls
- ◆ Vaulted master bedroom features a large walk-in closet, spa tub, separate shower room and access to the rear patio
- ◆ Covered entrance opens into the foyer with a large greeting area
- ◆ Formal living room with 12' ceiling and 36" walls on two sides
- ◆ Island kitchen features a large pantry and nook
- ◆ Cozy fireplace accents vaulted family room that opens onto a covered deck
- ◆ Utility room with generous space is adjacent to a half bath
- ◆ 3 bedrooms, 2 1/2 baths, 3-car garage
- ◆ Crawl space foundation

Price Code E

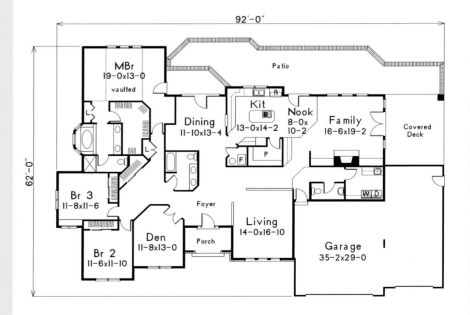

To order this plan, visit the Menards Building Materials Desk.

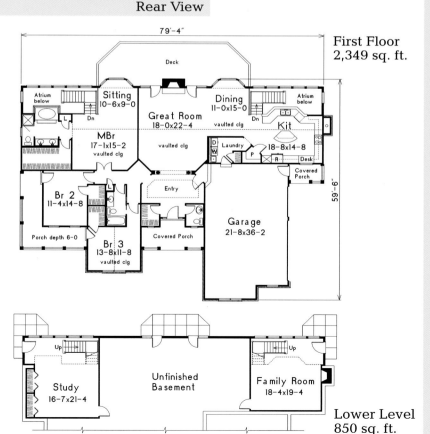

Rear View

First Floor
2,349 sq. ft.

79'-4"

Deck

Atrium below

Sitting
10-6x9-0

Dining
11-0x15-0

Atrium below

Great Room
18-0x22-4
vaulted clg

Kit
18-8x14-8

MBr
17-1x15-2
vaulted clg

vaulted clg

Laundry

Desk

Covered Porch

Entry

Br 2
11-4x14-8

59'-6"

Porch depth 6-0

Garage
21-8x36-2

Br 3
13-8x11-8
vaulted clg

Covered Porch

Study
16-7x21-4

Unfinished
Basement

Family Room
18-4x19-4

Lower Level
850 sq. ft.

Lakeport

Double Atrium Embraces The Sun

3,199 total square feet of living area

Special features

◆ Grand-scale kitchen features bay-shaped cabinetry built over an atrium that overlooks a two-story window wall

◆ A second atrium dominates the master bedroom that boasts a sitting area with bay window as well as a luxurious bath that has a whirlpool tub open to the garden atrium and lower level study

◆ 3 bedrooms, 2 1/2 baths, 3-car side entry garage

◆ Walk-out basement foundation

Price Code E

To order this plan, visit the Menards Building Materials Desk.

Sugarcreek

Bright, Spacious Plan With Many Features

2,308 total square feet of living area

Special features

◆ Efficient kitchen designed with many cabinets and large walk-in pantry adjoins the family/breakfast area featuring a beautiful fireplace

◆ A double-door entry leads into the luxurious master bedroom which features two walk-in closets and a beautiful bath

◆ Living room includes a vaulted ceiling, fireplace and a sunny atrium window wall creating a dramatic atmosphere

◆ 2" x 6" exterior walls available, please order plan #M01-058D-0077

◆ 3 bedrooms, 2 baths, 2-car side entry garage

◆ Walk-out basement foundation

Price Code D

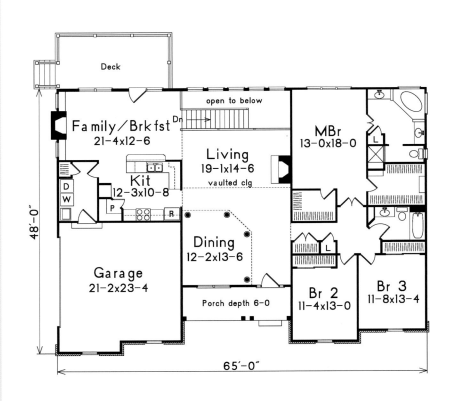

To order this plan, visit the Menards Building Materials Desk.

MENARDS

Lewiston

Large Family-Sized Kitchen Is Centrally Located

2,731 total square feet of living area

Special features

◆ Isolated master bedroom enjoys double walk-in closets, a coffered ceiling and an elegant bath
◆ Both dining and living rooms feature coffered ceilings and bay windows
◆ Breakfast room includes a dramatic vaulted ceiling and plenty of windows
◆ Family room features fireplace flanked by shelves, vaulted ceiling and access to rear deck
◆ Secondary bedrooms are separate from living areas
◆ 4 bedrooms, 3 1/2 baths, 2-car side entry garage
◆ Basement foundation

Price Code E

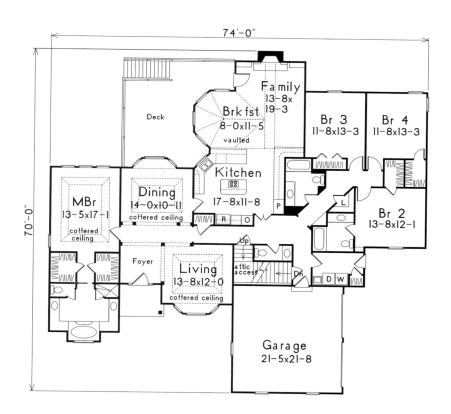

To order this plan, visit the Menards Building Materials Desk.

Stoneridge

Country Flavor With Atrium

2,384 total square feet of living area

Special features

- ◆ Bracketed box windows create an exterior with country charm
- ◆ Massive-sized great room features a majestic atrium, fireplace, box window wall, dining balcony and a vaulted ceiling
- ◆ An atrium balcony with large bay window off the deck is enjoyed by the spacious breakfast room
- ◆ 1,038 square feet of optional living area below with family room, wet bar, bedroom #4 and bath
- ◆ 3 bedrooms, 2 1/2 baths, 2-car side entry garage
- ◆ Walk-out basement foundation

Price Code D

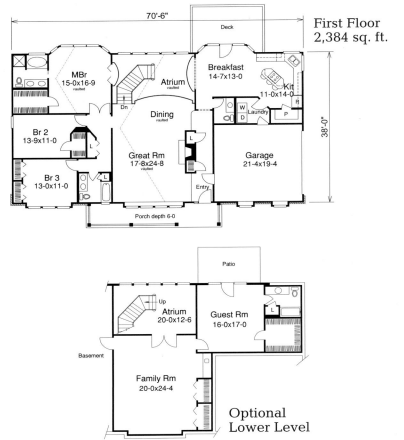

First Floor
2,384 sq. ft.

Optional Lower Level

To order this plan, visit the Menards Building Materials Desk.

Grantshire

Gallery Opens Into Grand Living Room

2,648 total square feet of living area

Special features

◆ Energy efficient home with 2" x 6" exterior walls
◆ Private study has access to the master bedroom and porch
◆ Grand-sized living room features a sloped ceiling, fireplace and entry to porches
◆ Master bedroom boasts an expansive bath with separate vanities, large walk-in closet and separate tub and shower units
◆ Large kitchen includes an eating area and breakfast bar
◆ Large utility room features extra counterspace and a storage closet
◆ 3 bedrooms, 2 baths, 2-car carport
◆ Crawl space foundation, drawings also include slab foundation

Price Code E

To order this plan, visit the Menards Building Materials Desk.

Hullverson

Appealing Ranch

1,414 total square feet of living area

Special features

- ◆ 9' ceilings throughout the first floor
- ◆ Vaulted ceilings add spaciousness to the family room, kitchen/breakfast area and master bedroom
- ◆ The secluded master bedroom enjoys a walk-in closet and expansive bath with a double vanity, whirlpool tub and linen closet
- ◆ 3 bedrooms, 2 baths, 2-car garage
- ◆ Basement foundation

Price Code A

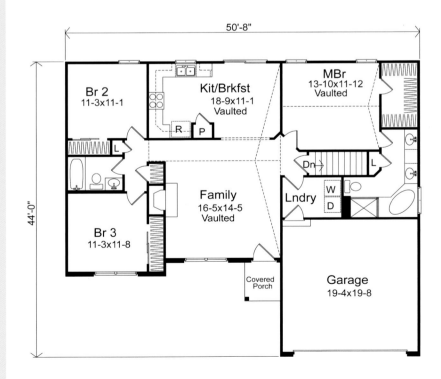

To order this plan, visit the Menards Building Materials Desk.

Plan #M01-001D-0048

MENARDS

Squire I

Spacious Interior For Open Living

1,400 total square feet of living area

Special features
- ◆ Front porch offers warmth and welcome
- ◆ Large great room opens into the dining room creating an open living atmosphere
- ◆ Kitchen features convenient laundry area, pantry and breakfast bar
- ◆ 2" x 6" exterior walls available, please order plan #M01-001D-0103
- ◆ 3 bedrooms, 2 baths, 2-car garage
- ◆ Crawl space foundation, drawings also include basement and slab foundations

Price Code A

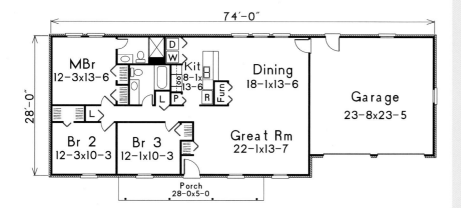

To order this plan, visit the Menards Building Materials Desk.

147

Clayton Manor

Rambling Ranch With Country Charm

2,514 total square feet of living area

Special features

◆ An expansive porch welcomes you to the foyer, spacious dining area with bay and a gallery-sized hall with plant shelf above

◆ A highly functional U-shaped kitchen is open to a bayed breakfast room, study and family room with a 46' vista

◆ The family will enjoy time spent in the vaulted rear sunroom with fireplace

◆ 1,509 square feet of optional living area on the lower level with recreation room, bedroom #4 with bath and an office with storage closet

◆ 3 bedrooms, 2 baths, 3-car side entry garage with workshop/storage area

◆ Walk-out basement foundation

Price Code D

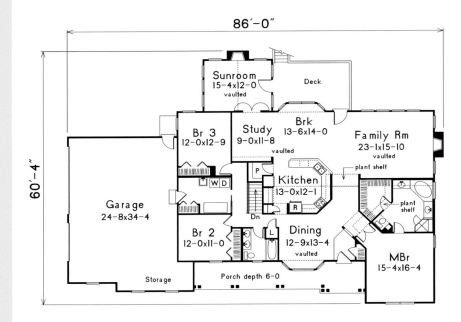

To order this plan, visit the Menards Building Materials Desk.

Canterhill

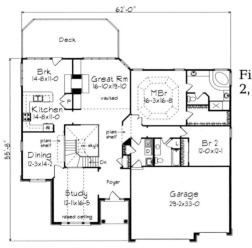

62'-0"

Deck

Brk
14-8x11-0

Great Rm
16-10x19-10
vaulted

MBr
16-3x16-8

Kitchen
14-8x11-0

plant shelf

Dining
12-3x14-2

skylt

Dn

Br 2
12-0x12-1

Study
12-11x16-5
raised ceiling

Foyer

Garage
29-2x33-0

55'-8"

First Floor
2,182 sq. ft.

Br 3
13-10x13-6

Family
16-2x18-7

Billard Rm
16-4x16-6

Atrium

Up

Wet Bar

Storage

Storage

Lower Level
1,229 sq. ft.

Lower Level Is Great For Entertaining

3,411 total square feet of living area

Special features

◆ Foyer opens to a large study with raised ceiling
◆ Master bedroom features an octagon-shaped raised ceiling and private bath with double vanities and corner whirlpool tub
◆ Expansive windows and a two-way fireplace enhance the great room
◆ 3 bedrooms, 3 baths, 3-car garage
◆ Basement foundation

Price Code F

To order this plan, visit the Menards Building Materials Desk.

Curtland

Appealing Ranch Has Attractive Front Dormers

1,642 total square feet of living area

Special features

- ◆ Walk-through kitchen boasts a vaulted ceiling and corner sink overlooking the family room
- ◆ Vaulted family room features a cozy fireplace and access to the rear patio
- ◆ Master bedroom includes a sloped ceiling, walk-in closet and private bath
- ◆ 3 bedrooms, 2 baths, 2-car garage
- ◆ Basement foundation, drawings also include slab and crawl space foundations

Price Code B

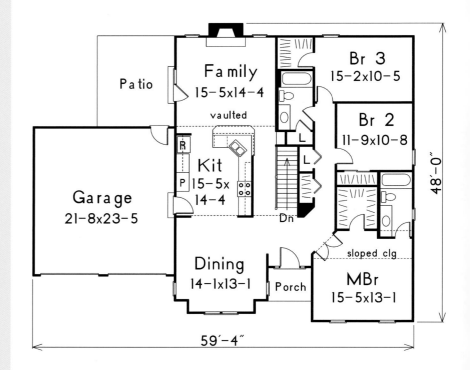

150

Haversham

Terrific Design For Family Living

1,345 total square feet of living area

Special features
◆ Brick front details add a touch of elegance
◆ Master bedroom has a private full bath
◆ Great room combines with the dining area creating a sense of spaciousness
◆ Garage includes a handy storage area which could easily convert to a workshop space
◆ 3 bedrooms, 2 baths, 2-car side entry garage
◆ Basement foundation, drawings also include crawl space and slab foundations

Price Code A

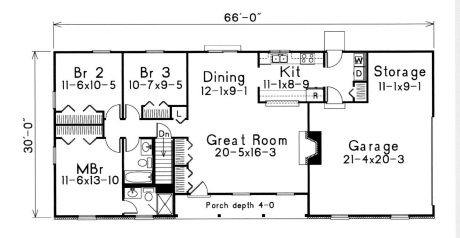

66'-0"

30'-0"

Br 2
11-6x10-5

Br 3
10-7x9-5

Dining
12-1x9-1

Kit
11-1x8-9

Storage
11-1x9-1

W
D

R

L

Dn

MBr
11-6x13-10

Great Room
20-5x16-3

Garage
21-4x20-3

Porch depth 4-0

Shrewsbury

Ranch Layout Has Two Separate Living Quarters

1,736 total square feet of living area

Special features

◆ Vaulted master bedroom features a double-door entry and private bath
◆ Garage apartment comes complete with adjacent terrace and porch
◆ Windows surround the cozy dining room for added sunshine
◆ 3 bedrooms, 3 baths, 2-car garage
◆ Slab foundation

Price Code B

Rear View

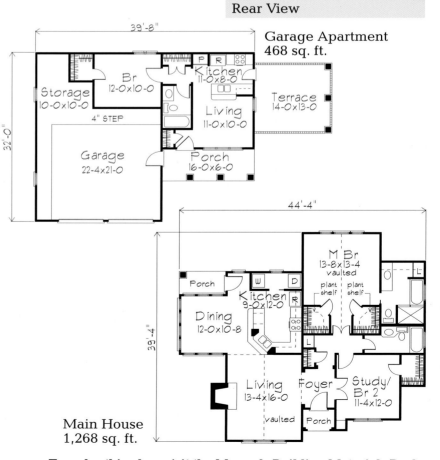

Garage Apartment
468 sq. ft.

39'-8"

32'-0"

Storage 10-0x10-0
Br 12-0x10-0
Kitchen 11-0x8-0
Terrace 14-0x13-0

4" STEP

Garage 22-4x21-0
Living 11-0x10-0
Porch 16-0x6-0

Main House
1,268 sq. ft.

44'-4"

39'-4"

Porch
Kitchen 9-0x12-0
M Br 13-8x13-4 vaulted
plant shelf   plant shelf

Dining 12-0x10-8

Living 13-4x16-0
Foyer
Study/ Br 2 11-4x12-0
vaulted   Porch

152

To order this plan, visit the Menards Building Materials Desk.

MENARDS

Hawkins

Inviting Covered Corner Entry

1,042 total square feet of living area

Special features
- Living room is brightened by several windows
- Spacious kitchen includes a laundry closet and space for dining
- Front entry has a handy coat closet
- Plenty of extra storage space is located in the garage
- 2 bedrooms, 1 bath, 2-car garage
- Basement foundation, drawings also include crawl space and slab foundations

Price Code AA

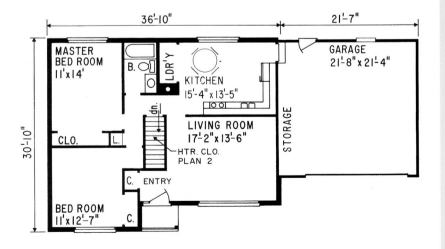

To order this plan, visit the Menards Building Materials Desk.

Gardenview

Dining In A Garden

2,563 total square feet of living area

Special features
◆ Contemporary facade with traditional flair
◆ Impressive 13' high volume ceilings in grand entry and sunken living room
◆ Breathtaking garden room with dining island features vaulted skylit ceiling, surrounding window wall and hidden whirlpool retreat off the master bedroom
◆ Vaulted master bedroom includes view of garden and lavish bath
◆ 3 bedrooms, 2 baths, 2-car garage
◆ Basement foundation

Price Code D

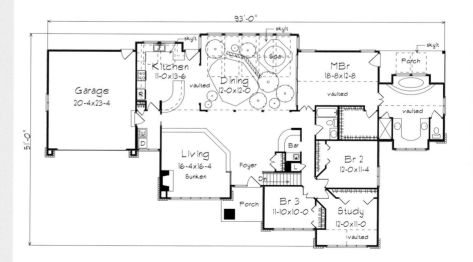

Dining Room

To order this plan, visit the Menards Building Materials Desk.

Windham

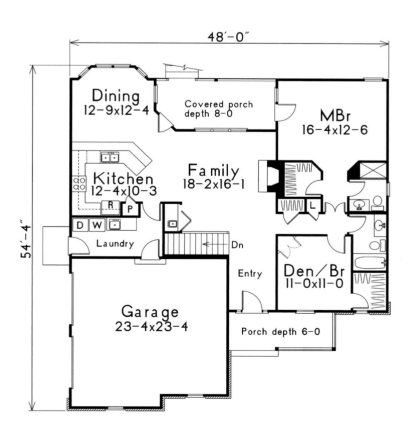

Flexible Design Is Popular

1,440 total square feet of living area

Special features

◆ Open floor plan with access to covered porches in front and back

◆ Lots of linen, pantry and closet space throughout

◆ Laundry/mud room between kitchen and garage is a convenient feature

◆ 2 bedrooms, 2 baths, 2-car side entry garage

◆ Basement foundation

Price Code A

To order this plan, visit the Menards Building Materials Desk.

Littleton

Three-Way Design

588 total square feet of living area

Special features
◆ May be built as a duplex, 4-car garage or apartment garage/vacation cabin as shown
◆ Very livable plan in a small footprint
◆ Living room features a functional entry, bayed dining area, corner fireplace and opens to kitchen with breakfast bar
◆ 1 bedroom, 1 bath, 2-car side entry garage
◆ Slab foundation
◆ 1,176 square feet of living area when built as a duplex

Price Code AAA

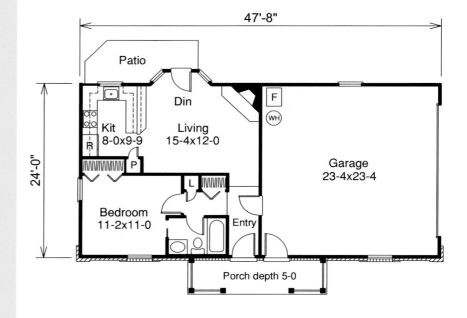

Alameda

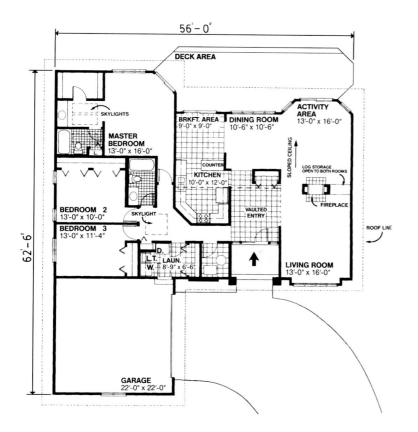

Floridian Style Home

1,932 total square feet of living area

Special features

- ◆ Large see-through fireplace warms and beautifies the entire living area
- ◆ Skylights bring sun to the hallway and master bath
- ◆ Sliding glass doors in the activity and breakfast areas lead to a large, open deck
- ◆ 3 bedrooms, 2 baths, 2-car side entry garage
- ◆ Partial basement/crawl space foundation, drawings also include crawl space foundation

Price Code C

To order this plan, visit the Menards Building Materials Desk.

Squire II

Spacious Interior For Open Living

1,400 total square feet of living area

Special features

◆ Front porch offers warmth and welcome

◆ Large great room opens into the dining room creating an open living atmosphere

◆ Kitchen features convenient laundry area, pantry and breakfast bar

◆ 2" x 6" exterior walls available, please order plan #M01-001D-0104

◆ 3 bedrooms, 2 baths, 2-car garage

◆ Crawl space foundation, drawings also include basement and slab foundations

Price Code A

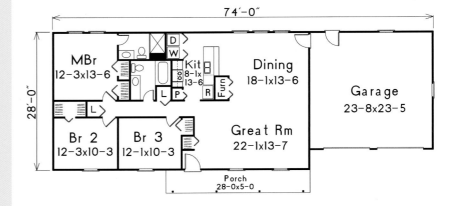

MENARDS

Fairview

Practical Layout

1,883 total square feet of living area

Special features

◆ Energy efficient home with 2" x 6" exterior walls
◆ Large laundry room located off the garage has a coat closet and half bath
◆ Large family room with fireplace and access to the covered porch is a great central gathering room
◆ U-shaped kitchen has breakfast bar, large pantry and swing door to dining room for convenient serving
◆ 3 bedrooms, 2 1/2 baths, 2-car side entry garage
◆ Basement foundation

Price Code C

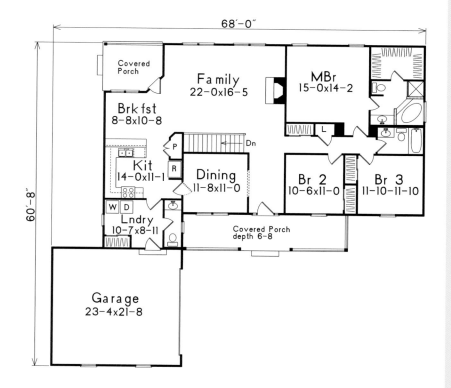

To order this plan, visit the Menards Building Materials Desk.

Bridgeton

Stylish And Distinctive Plan

2,513 total square feet of living area

Special features

◆ Coffered ceilings in master bedroom, living and dining rooms
◆ Kitchen features island cooktop and built-in desk
◆ Dramatic vaulted ceiling in the breakfast room is framed by plenty of windows
◆ Covered entry porch leads into spacious foyer
◆ Family room features an impressive fireplace and vaulted ceiling that joins the breakfast room creating a spacious entertainment area
◆ 4 bedrooms, 2 full baths, 2 half baths, 2-car side entry garage
◆ Basement foundation

Price Code D

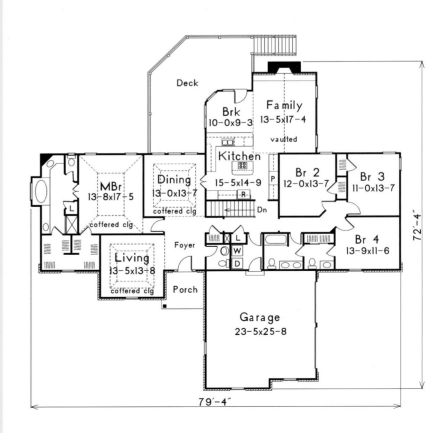

MENARDS

Solarium

Unique One-Story With Solarium Bath

2,859 total square feet of living area

Special features
- The vaulted great room with fireplace includes sliding glass doors that lead to covered and uncovered patio areas and the stairwell that provides access to the unfinished lower level
- A walk-in pantry, menu/computer desk and snack island are a few highlights of the kitchen
- The vaulted master bedroom includes a posh bath with separate toilet and shower areas, a "bath-in-a-solarium" with plant shelves and skylights above and sliding glass doors to a rear patio
- 3 bedrooms, 2 1/2 baths, 3-car side entry garage
- Basement foundation

Price Code E

Montclaire

Massive Ranch With Classy Features

2,874 total square feet of living area

Special features

- ◆ Large family room with sloped ceiling and wood beams adjoins the kitchen and breakfast area with windows on two walls
- ◆ Large foyer opens to the family room with a massive stone fireplace and open stairs to the basement
- ◆ Private master bedroom includes a raised tub under the bay window, dramatic dressing area and a huge walk-in closet
- ◆ 4 bedrooms, 2 1/2 baths, 2-car side entry garage
- ◆ Basement foundation

Price Code E

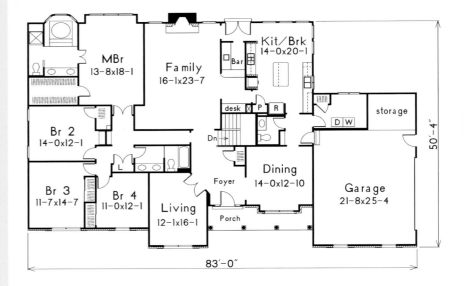

To order this plan, visit the Menards Building Materials Desk.

Sherwood

Large Corner Deck Lends Way To Outdoor Living Area

1,283 total square feet of living area

Special features
- ◆ Vaulted breakfast room has sliding doors that open onto deck
- ◆ Kitchen features convenient corner sink and pass-through to dining room
- ◆ Open living atmosphere in dining area and great room
- ◆ Vaulted great room features a fireplace
- ◆ 3 bedrooms, 2 baths, 2-car garage
- ◆ Basement foundation

Price Code A

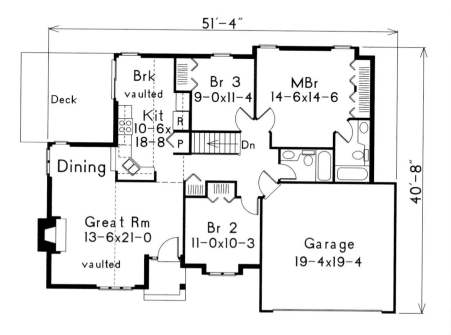

Sunfield

Private Master Bedroom Has A Grand Bath

1,856 total square feet of living area

Special features

- ◆ Energy efficient home with 2" x 6" exterior walls
- ◆ Living room features include fireplace, 12' ceiling and skylights
- ◆ Common vaulted ceiling creates an open atmosphere in the kitchen and breakfast room
- ◆ Garage with storage areas conveniently accesses home through handy utility room
- ◆ Private hall separates secondary bedrooms from living areas
- ◆ 3 bedrooms, 2 baths, 2-car side entry garage
- ◆ Slab foundation, drawings also include crawl space foundation

Price Code C

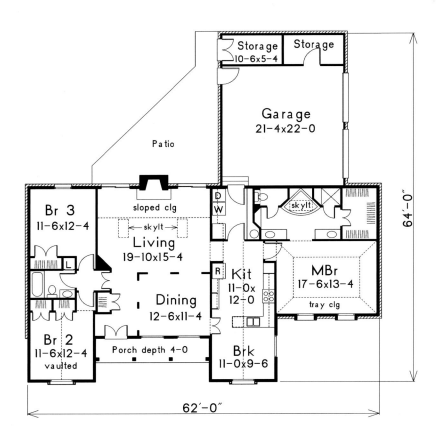

To order this plan, visit the Menards Building Materials Desk.

Plan #M01-001D-0079

Madison

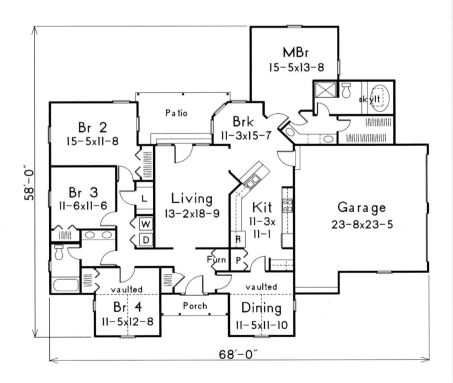

Angled Walls Create Dramatic Layout

2,080 total square feet of living area

Special features
◆ Combined design elements create a unique facade
◆ Foyer leads into large living room and direct view to patio
◆ Master bedroom includes spacious bath with garden tub, separate shower, walk-in closet and dressing area
◆ 2" x 6" exterior walls available, please order plan #M01-001-0126
◆ 4 bedrooms, 2 baths, 2-car side entry garage
◆ Crawl space foundation, drawings also include basement and slab foundations

Price Code C

To order this plan, visit the Menards Building Materials Desk.

Lawrenceville

Big Features In A Small Package

1,941 total square feet of living area

Special features
◆ Dramatic, exciting and spacious interior
◆ Vaulted great room is brightened by a sunken atrium window wall and skylights
◆ Vaulted U-shaped gourmet kitchen with plant shelf opens to dining room
◆ First floor half bath features space for a stackable washer and dryer
◆ 4 bedrooms, 2 1/2 baths, 2-car garage
◆ Walk-out basement foundation

Price Code C

Lower Level
945 sq. ft.

First Floor
996 sq. ft.

To order this plan, visit the Menards Building Materials Desk.

MENARDS

Barrington

Active Living Areas Throughout

3,808 total square feet of living area

Special features

◆ Cozy hearth room shares fireplace with great room
◆ See-through fireplace connects gathering areas
◆ Master bath features stylish angled glass block walls that frame private toilet and large shower
◆ 3 bedrooms, 3 baths, 2-car garage
◆ Basement foundation

Price Code F

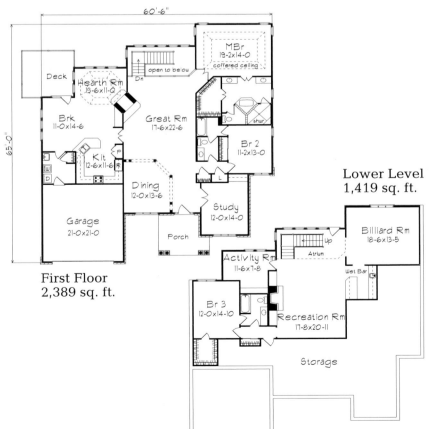

First Floor
2,389 sq. ft.

Lower Level
1,419 sq. ft.

To order this plan, visit the Menards Building Materials Desk.

Hillsboro

Compact Layout, Amenity Full

1,567 total square feet of living area

Special features

◆ Front gables and extended porch add charm to facade

◆ Large bay windows add brightness to breakfast and dining rooms

◆ The master bath boasts an oversized tub, separate shower, double sinks and large walk-in closet

◆ Living room features a vaulted ceiling and a prominent fireplace

◆ 3 bedrooms, 2 baths, 2-car drive under garage

◆ Basement foundation

Price Code B

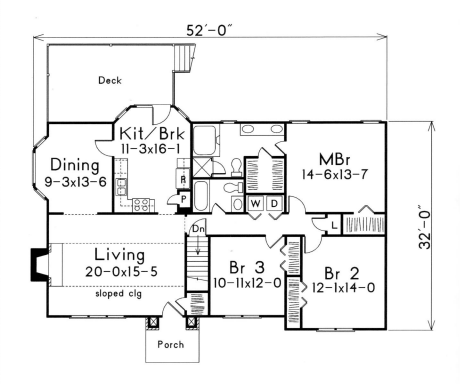

To order this plan, visit the Menards Building Materials Desk.

Carrmont

Well-Designed Family Living

1,441 total square feet of living area

Special features
◆ Combined living and dining rooms offer plenty of open space for large family gatherings
◆ Functional kitchen opens to a nice-sized family room with sliding glass doors opening to the rear patio
◆ Master bedroom offers a private bath and the secondary bedrooms share a hall bath
◆ Convenient utility room opens to the front foyer and garage
◆ 3 bedrooms, 2 baths, 2-car garage
◆ Basement foundation, drawings also include crawl space and slab foundations

Price Code A

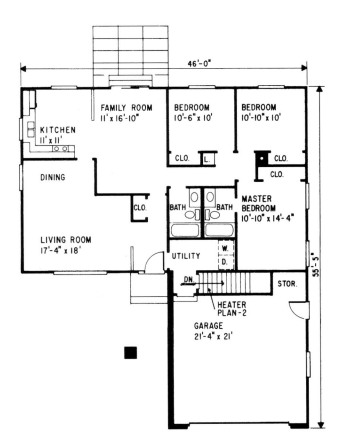

Briarview

Simplicity With Livability

1,365 total square feet of living area

Special features

◆ Home is easily adaptable for physical accessibility featuring no stairs and extra-wide hall baths, laundry and garage

◆ Living room has separate entry and opens to a spacious dining room with view of rear patio

◆ L-shaped kitchen is well-equipped and includes a built-in pantry

◆ All bedrooms are spaciously sized and offer generous closet storage

◆ 3 bedrooms, 2 baths, 1-car garage

◆ Slab foundation

Price Code A

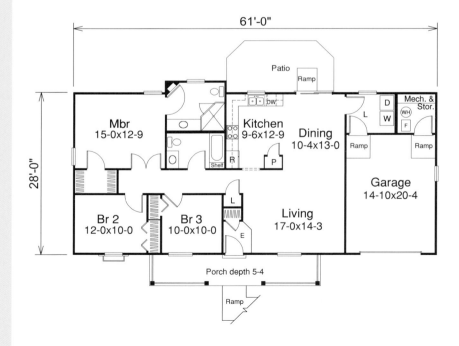

To order this plan, visit the Menards Building Materials Desk.

Compton Park

Atrium One-Story

1,973 total square feet of living area

Special features

- ◆ The impressive great room includes a vaulted ceiling, fireplace and 10' high feature windows
- ◆ A center island, built-in pantry and corner sink with windows are a few amenities of the kitchen that has access to a large deck
- ◆ The morning/breakfast room includes a see-through fireplace and balcony overlook of the atrium and rear yard through a 13' x 14' feature window wall
- ◆ The master bedroom suite offers an expansive bay window, convenient linen closet and luxury bath
- ◆ 4 bedrooms, 2 1/2 baths, 2-car side entry garage
- ◆ Walk-out basement foundation, drawings also include slab and crawl space foundations

Price Code D

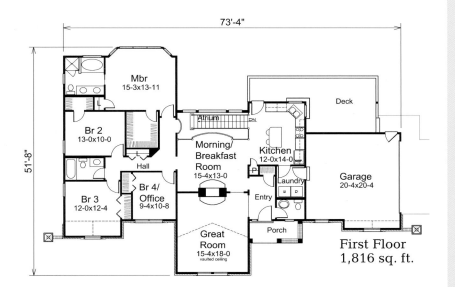

First Floor
1,816 sq. ft.

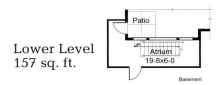

Lower Level
157 sq. ft.

To order this plan, visit the Menards Building Materials Desk.

171

Lakemont

Ranch Of Enchantment

1,559 total square feet of living area

Special features

◆ A cozy country appeal is provided by a spacious porch, masonry fireplace, roof dormers and a perfect balance of stonework and siding

◆ Large living room enjoys a fireplace, bayed dining area and separate entry

◆ A U-shaped kitchen is adjoined by a breakfast room with bay window and large pantry

◆ 3 bedrooms, 2 1/2 baths, 2-car drive under side entry garage

◆ Basement foundation

Price Code B

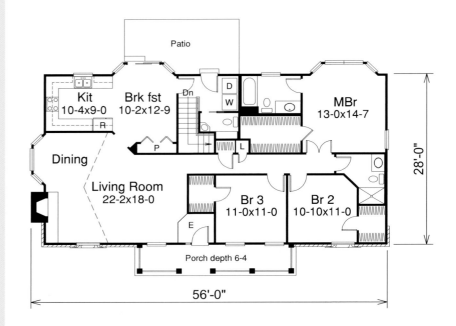

To order this plan, visit the Menards Building Materials Desk.

Olsen

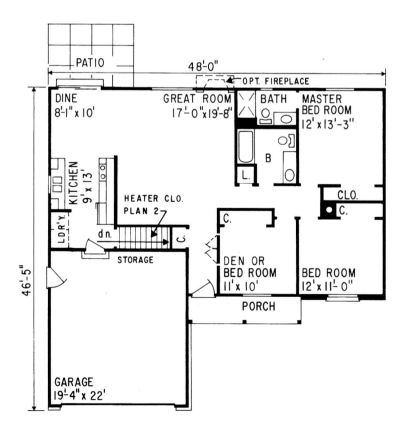

Classic Ranch With Inviting Covered Front Porch

1,317 total square feet of living area

Special features
- Galley-style kitchen includes substantial cabinets and counterspace
- Dining area is joined by the great room creating an open atmosphere
- The lovely patio off the dining area brings the outdoors in
- A well-designed laundry area is nestled between the garage and kitchen
- 3 bedrooms, 2 baths, 2-car garage
- Basement foundation, drawings also include crawl space and slab foundations

Price Code A

To order this plan, visit the Menards Building Materials Desk.

Rosehill

A Cottage
With Class

576 total square feet of living area

Special features

- Perfect country retreat features vaulted living room and entry with skylights and a plant shelf above
- A double-door entry leads to the vaulted bedroom with bath access
- Kitchen offers generous storage and pass-through breakfast bar
- 1 bedroom, 1 bath
- Crawl space foundation

Price Code AAA

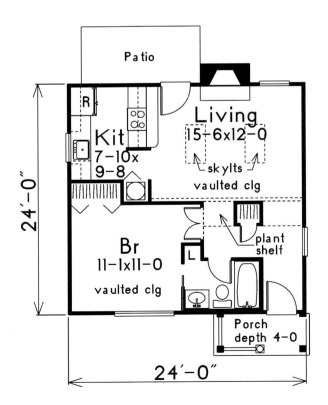

Cypress

Multiple Gabled Roofs Add Drama

1,533 total square feet of living area

Special features
◆ Master bedroom accesses the outdoors through sliding glass doors onto a deck
◆ A sloped ceiling adds volume to the large activity area
◆ Activity area has fireplace, snack bar and shares access to the outdoors with the master bedroom
◆ Convenient utility room located near the garage
◆ 3 bedrooms, 2 baths, 2-car garage
◆ Partial basement foundation, drawings also include crawl space foundation

Price Code B

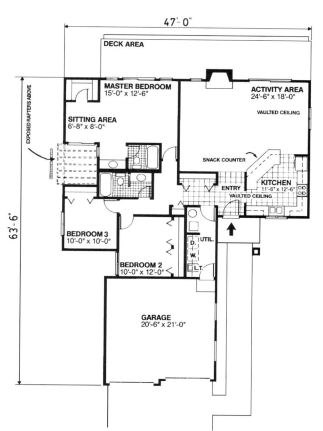

47'-0"

DECK AREA

MASTER BEDROOM
15'-0" x 12'-6"

ACTIVITY AREA
24'-6" x 18'-0"

VAULTED CEILING

SITTING AREA
6'-8" x 8'-0"

EXPOSED RAFTERS ABOVE

SNACK COUNTER

ENTRY

KITCHEN
11'-6" x 12'-6"

VAULTED CEILING

63'-6"

BEDROOM 3
10'-0" x 10'-0"

UTIL.

D.
W.

BEDROOM 2
10'-0" x 12'-0"

GARAGE
20'-6" x 21'-0"

Plan #M01-001D-0044

Cumberland

Distinctive Design, Convenient Floor Plan

1,375 total square feet of living area

Special features

◆ Attractive gables highlight home's exterior
◆ Centrally located living room with bay area
◆ Master bedroom features patio access, double walk-in-closets and private bath
◆ Side entry garage includes handy storage area
◆ 2" x 6" exterior walls available, please order plan #M01-001D-0101
◆ 3 bedrooms, 2 baths, 2-car side entry garage
◆ Crawl space foundation, drawings also include basement and slab foundations

Price Code A

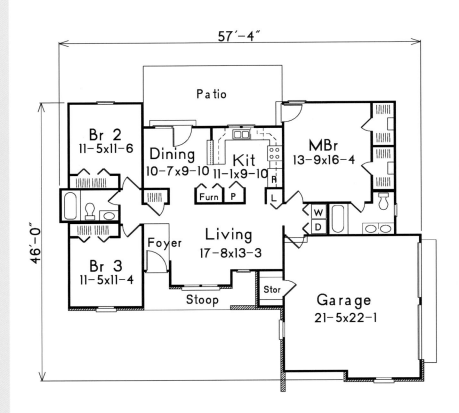

57'-4"

46'-0"

Patio

Br 2
11-5x11-6

Dining
10-7x9-10

Kit
11-1x9-10

MBr
13-9x16-4

Furn   P

Br 3
11-5x11-4

Foyer

Living
17-8x13-3

W
D

Stoop   Stor

Garage
21-5x22-1

To order this plan, visit the Menards Building Materials Desk.

Ridgecrest

Home Features Generous Room Sizes

2,164 total square feet of living area

Special features

- Great design for entertaining with a wet bar and see-through fireplace in the great room
- Plenty of closet space
- Vaulted ceilings enlarge the master bedroom, great room and kitchen/breakfast area
- Great room features great view to the rear of the home
- 2" x 6" exterior walls available, please order plan #M01-058D-0083
- 3 bedrooms, 2 1/2 baths, 2-car side entry garage
- Basement foundation

Price Code C

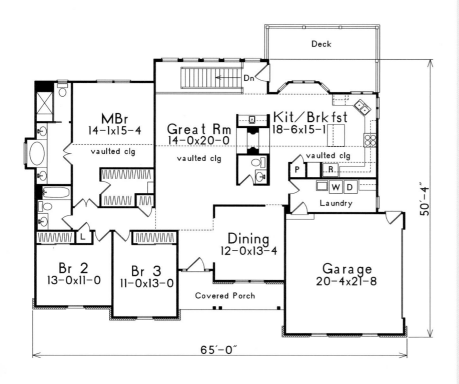

Deck

Dn

MBr
14-1x15-4
vaulted clg

Great Rm
14-0x20-0
vaulted clg

Kit/Brkfst
18-6x15-1
vaulted clg

P   R

W D

Laundry

50'-4"

Br 2
13-0x11-0

Br 3
11-0x13-0

Dining
12-0x13-4

Garage
20-4x21-8

Covered Porch

65'-0"

To order this plan, visit the Menards Building Materials Desk.

Carrollstone

Dramatic Country Architecture

2,100 total square feet of living area

Special features

◆ A large courtyard with stone walls, lantern columns and covered porch welcomes you into open spaces

◆ The great room features a stone fireplace, built-in shelves, vaulted ceiling and atrium with dramatic staircase and a two and a half story window wall

◆ Two walk-in closets, vaulted ceiling with plant shelf and a luxury bath adorn the master bedroom suite

◆ 1,391 square feet of optional living area on the lower level with family room, walk-in bar, sitting area, bedroom #3 and a bath

◆ 2 bedrooms, 2 baths, 3-car side entry garage

◆ Walk-out basement foundation

Price Code C

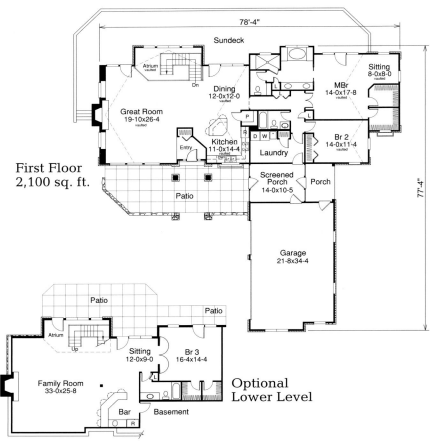

First Floor
2,100 sq. ft.

Optional
Lower Level

To order this plan, visit the Menards Building Materials Desk.

MENARDS

Woodlawn

High Ceilings Create Openness

2,516 total square feet of living area

Special features

◆ 12' ceilings in the living areas
◆ Plenty of closet space in this open ranch plan
◆ Large kitchen/breakfast area joins great room via the see-through fireplace creating two large entering spaces flanking each side
◆ Large three-car garage has extra storage area
◆ The master bedroom has an eye-catching bay window
◆ 3 bedrooms, 2 1/2 baths, 3-car garage
◆ Basement foundation

Price Code D

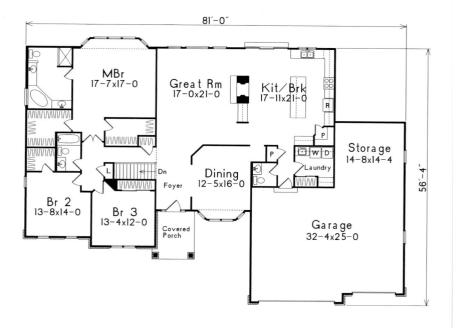

To order this plan, visit the Menards Building Materials Desk.

Malabar Bay

Lavish Master Bath With Private Garden

2,767 total square feet of living area

Special features

◆ The huge great room enjoys a fireplace and vaulted ceiling

◆ The kitchen is second-to-none including a wrap-around snack bar and walk-in corner pantry

◆ Flanked by large covered patios, the breakfast room is drenched by sunlight through a wall of windows

◆ The master bedroom offers an incredible bath that showcases a shower surrounded by a private garden

◆ 3 bedrooms, 3 baths, 3-car side entry garage

◆ Crawl space foundation, drawings also include slab and basement foundations

Price Code E

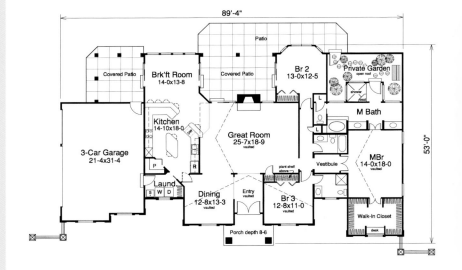

To order this plan, visit the Menards Building Materials Desk.

Pinehurst II

Large Living And Dining Area

1,160 total square feet of living area

Special features
- U-shaped kitchen has breakfast bar and convenient laundry area
- Master bedroom has private half bath and large closet
- Dining room features handy access to the outdoors
- Open living atmosphere is created by the adjoining dining area and great room
- 3 bedrooms, 1 1/2 baths
- Crawl space foundation, drawings also include basement and slab foundations

Price Code AA

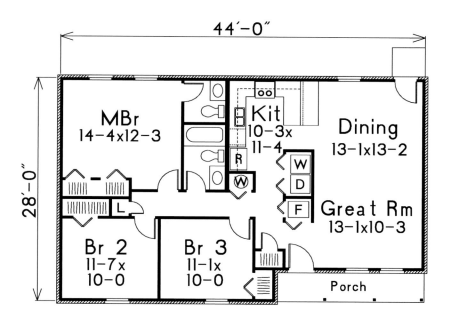

To order this plan, visit the Menards Building Materials Desk.

Plan #M01-007D-0119

MENARDS

Hearthwood

Sensational Home Designed For Views

1,621 total square feet of living area

Special features

- ◆ The front exterior includes an attractive gable-end arched window and extra-deep porch
- ◆ A grand-scale great room enjoys a coffered ceiling, fireplace, access to the wrap-around deck and is brightly lit with numerous French doors and windows
- ◆ The master bedroom suite has a sitting area, double walk-in closets and a luxury bath
- ◆ 223 square feet of optional finished space on the lower level
- ◆ 3 bedrooms, 2 baths, 2-car drive under side entry garage
- ◆ Basement foundation

Price Code B

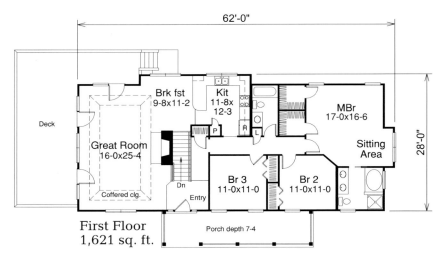

First Floor
1,621 sq. ft.

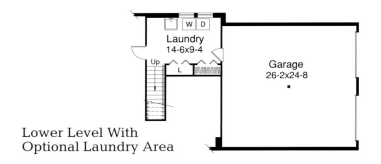

Lower Level With
Optional Laundry Area

182

To order this plan, visit the Menards Building Materials Desk.

Donohue

Open Floor Plan Makes Home Feel Larger

1,277 total square feet of living area

Special features
◆ Energy efficient home with 2" x 6" exterior walls
◆ Vaulted ceilings grace the master bedroom, great room, kitchen and dining room
◆ Laundry closet is located near the bedrooms for convenience
◆ Compact, yet efficient kitchen
◆ 3 bedrooms, 2 baths, 2-car garage
◆ Basement foundation

Price Code A

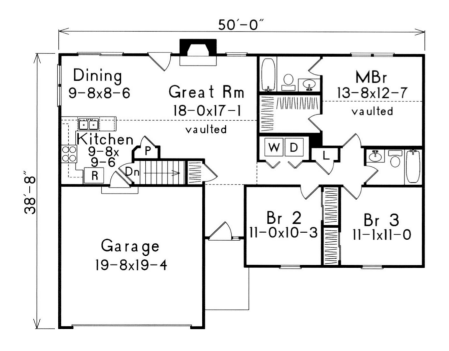

50'-0"

38'-8"

Dining
9-8x8-6

Great Rm
18-0x17-1
vaulted

MBr
13-8x12-7
vaulted

Kitchen
9-8x
9-6

W D   L

Br 2
11-0x10-3

Br 3
11-1x11-0

Garage
19-8x19-4

P
Dn
R

To order this plan, visit the Menards Building Materials Desk.

183

MENARDS

Maitland

Interesting Plan With A Decorative Dormer

1,516 total square feet of living area

Special features

- ◆ Spacious great room is open to dining area with a bay and unique stair location
- ◆ Attractive and well-planned kitchen offers breakfast bar and built-in pantry
- ◆ Smartly designed master bedroom enjoys patio view
- ◆ 3 bedrooms, 2 baths, 2-car garage
- ◆ Basement foundation

Price Code B

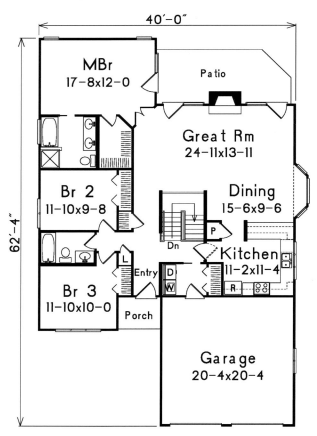

To order this plan, visit the Menards Building Materials Desk.

Rear View

Ashbury

Cozy Breakfast Bay With Full Outside View

2,397 total square feet of living area

Special features

- Varied ceiling heights throughout home
- All bedrooms boast walk-in closets
- Garage includes convenient storage area
- Angled kitchen counter overlooks spacious living room with fireplace
- Master bedroom has coffered ceiling and luxurious bath
- 4 bedrooms, 3 baths, 2-car side entry garage
- Slab foundation

Price Code D

To order this plan, visit the Menards Building Materials Desk.

Vernon Hills

Rustic Facade

1,550 total square feet of living area

Special features

◆ Convenient mud room between the garage and kitchen

◆ Oversized dining area allows plenty of space for entertaining

◆ Master bedroom has a private bath and ample closet space

◆ Large patio off the family room brings the outdoors in

◆ 3 bedrooms, 2 baths, 2-car side entry garage

◆ Basement foundation, drawings also include crawl space or slab foundations

Price Code B

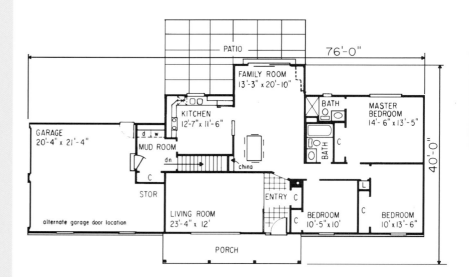

To order this plan, visit the Menards Building Materials Desk.

Summerdale

Cottage With Screened Porch, Garage And Shop

1,072 total square feet of living area

Special features

- Integrated open and screened front porches guarantee comfortable summer enjoyment
- Oversized garage includes area for shop and miscellaneous storage
- U-shaped kitchen and breakfast area is adjacent to the vaulted living room and has access to screened porch through sliding glass doors
- 2 bedrooms, 2 baths, 2-car side entry garage
- Basement foundation
- 345 square feet of optional living area on the lower level including a third bedroom and a bath

Price Code AA

First Floor
1,072 sq. ft.

Optional
Lower Level

To order this plan, visit the Menards Building Materials Desk.

Shiloh Valley

Luxury Living In A Country Home

1,814 total square feet of living area

Special features

◆ This home enjoys a large country porch for a perfect leisure living area

◆ The vaulted great room, sunny breakfast room and kitchen with snack bar are all open to one another to create a very open sense of spaciousness

◆ A sensational lavish bath is the highlight of the master bedroom suite which features double vanities with a make-up counter, 5' x 5' shower with seat, separate toilet and a step-up whirlpool-in-a-sunroom

◆ 3 bedrooms, 2 baths, 3-car side entry garage

◆ Basement foundation

Price Code C

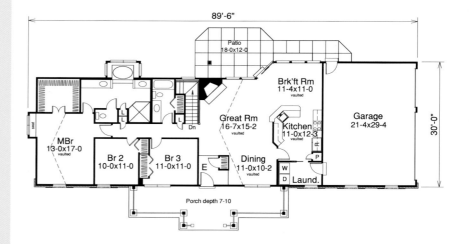

To order this plan, visit the Menards Building Materials Desk.

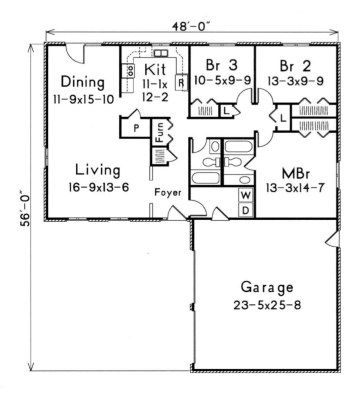

Monteray

L-Shaped Ranch With Many Amenities

1,440 total square feet of living area

Special features

- ◆ Spaciousness is created with open living and dining areas
- ◆ Entry foyer features a coat closet and half wall leading into the living area
- ◆ Walk-in pantry adds convenience to the U-shaped kitchen
- ◆ Spacious utility room is adjacent to the garage
- ◆ 3 bedrooms, 2 baths, 2-car side entry garage
- ◆ Crawl space foundation, drawings also include basement and slab foundations

Price Code A

To order this plan, visit the Menards Building Materials Desk.

Delmar

Family Living Focuses Around Central Fireplace

1,388 total square feet of living area

Special features

- ◆ Handsome see-through fireplace offers a gathering point for the kitchen, family and breakfast rooms
- ◆ Vaulted ceiling and large bay window in the master bedroom add charm to this room
- ◆ A dramatic angular wall and large windows add brightness to the kitchen and breakfast room
- ◆ Kitchen, breakfast and family rooms have vaulted ceilings, adding to this central living area
- ◆ 3 bedrooms, 2 baths, 2-car garage
- ◆ Crawl space foundation, drawings also include slab foundation

Price Code A

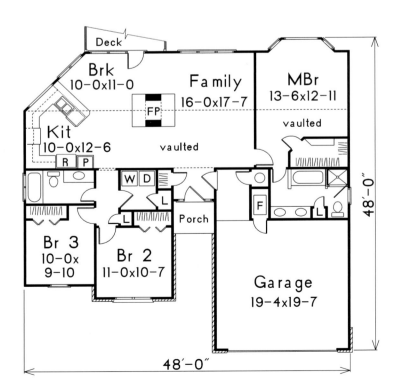

To order this plan, visit the Menards Building Materials Desk.

Courtland

Impressive Ranch Features Attractive Courtyard

2,851 total square feet of living area

Special features

◆ Foyer with double-door entrance leads to unique sunken living room with patio view
◆ Multi-purpose room is perfect for a home office, hobby room or fifth bedroom
◆ Master bedroom boasts abundant closet space and access to patio
◆ Family room has access to kitchen and features a fireplace flanked by windows
◆ 4 bedrooms, 3 baths, 2-car garage
◆ Basement foundation, drawings also include crawl space and slab foundations

Price Code E

To order this plan, visit the Menards Building Materials Desk.

191

Childress

Open Floor Plan For Family Activities

2,598 total square feet of living area

Special features

◆ A see-through fireplace warms the spacious great room, kitchen and breakfast area
◆ The private master bedroom enjoys two walk-in closets and a private bath with a whirlpool tub
◆ The study features a fireplace and is ideal for a home office
◆ A large walk-in pantry adds storage space to the kitchen
◆ 3 bedrooms, 2 1/2 baths, 2-car side entry garage
◆ Basement foundation

Price Code D

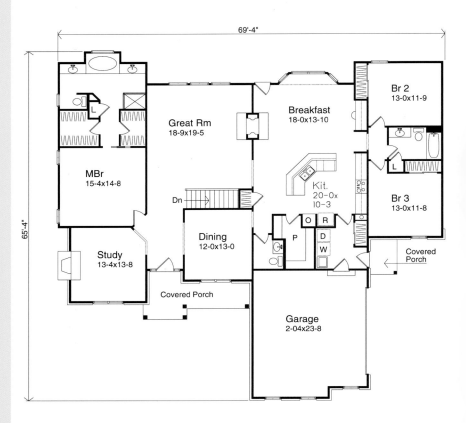

To order this plan, visit the Menards Building Materials Desk.

Oakshire

Contemporary Elegance With Efficiency

1,321 total square feet of living area

Special features

- Rear entry garage and elongated brick wall add to the appealing facade
- Dramatic vaulted living room includes corner fireplace and towering feature windows
- Breakfast room is immersed in light from two large windows and glass sliding doors
- 3 bedrooms, 2 baths, 1-car rear entry garage
- Basement foundation

Price Code A

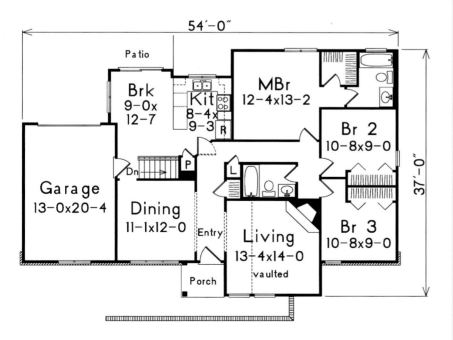

Patio

Brk
9-0x
12-7

Kit
8-4x
9-3

MBr
12-4x13-2

Br 2
10-8x9-0

Garage
13-0x20-4

Dining
11-1x12-0

Living
13-4x14-0
vaulted

Br 3
10-8x9-0

Entry

Porch

54'-0"

37'-0"

To order this plan, visit the Menards Building Materials Desk.

Miranda

Dormers Add Southern Accent

2,651 total square feet of living area

Special features

◆ Vaulted family room has a corner fireplace and access to the breakfast room and outdoor patio
◆ Dining room has a double-door entry from the covered front porch and a beautiful built-in corner display area
◆ Master bedroom has a 10' tray ceiling, private bath and two walk-in closets
◆ Kitchen has an enormous amount of counterspace with plenty of eating area and overlooks a cheerful breakfast room
◆ 3 bedrooms, 2 baths, 2-car side entry garage
◆ Basement foundation, drawings also include crawl space and slab foundations

Price Code E

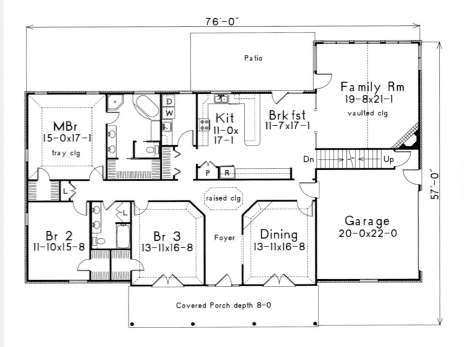

Cedar Lake

Impressive Home For Country Living

1,991 total square feet of living area

Special features

- A large porch with roof dormers and flanking stonework creates a distinctive country appeal
- The highly functional U-shaped kitchen is open to the dining and living rooms defined by a colonnade
- Large bay windows are enjoyed by both the living room and master bedroom
- Every bedroom features spacious walk-in closets and their own private bath
- 3 bedrooms, 3 1/2 baths, 2-car side entry garage
- Basement foundation

Price Code C

Patio

MBr
17-0x12-8

Living
21-0x16-6

Br 2
11-8x14-6

Dn

Garage
21-4x23-3

Kit
10-0 x 10-9

Brk fst
10-0x11-10

Br 3
15-8x12-6

Entry

Porch depth 6-0

38'-4"

85'-6"

Ashmont Place

Stylish Four Bedroom Ranch Plus Study

1,741 total square feet of living area

Special features

◆ Handsome exterior has multiple gables and elegant brickwork

◆ The great room offers a fireplace, vaulted ceiling and is open to the bayed dining area and kitchen with breakfast bar

◆ The master bedroom boasts a vaulted ceiling, large walk-in closet, luxury bath and enjoys a nearby room perfect for a study, nursery or fifth bedroom

◆ 4 bedrooms, 2 baths, 2-car garage

◆ Crawl space foundation, drawings also include slab and basement foundations

Price Code B

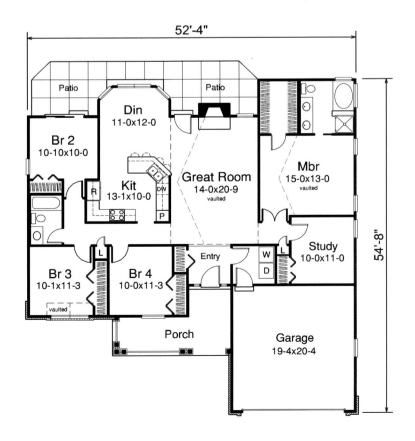

MENARDS

Hillshire

Split-Bedroom Floor Plan

1,242 total square feet of living area

Special features
- Energy efficient home with 2" x 6" exterior walls
- The wide foyer opens to the living room for a spacious atmosphere and grand first impression
- The centrally located kitchen easily serves the large dining and living rooms
- The split-bedroom design allows privacy for the homeowners who will love spending time in their master bedroom retreat
- 3 bedrooms, 2 baths, 2-car garage
- Basement foundation

Price Code A

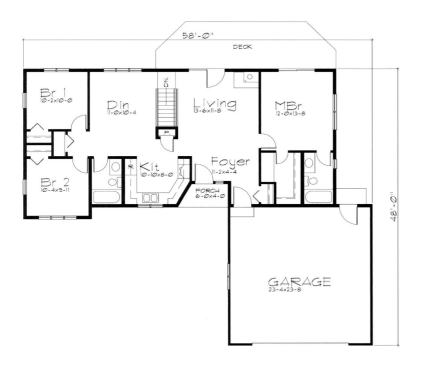

To order this plan, visit the Menards Building Materials Desk.

197

Timberview

Great Design For Vacation Home Or Year-Round Living

990 total square feet of living area

Special features

◆ Covered front porch adds a charming feel
◆ Vaulted ceilings in the kitchen, family and dining rooms create a spacious feel
◆ Large linen, pantry and storage closets throughout
◆ 2 bedrooms, 1 bath
◆ Crawl space foundation

Price Code AA

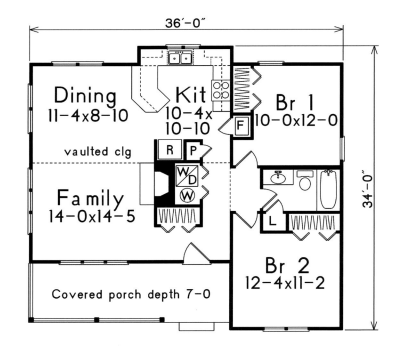

To order this plan, visit the Menards Building Materials Desk.

Cambridge

Front Bay Graces Dining Room

1,584 total square feet of living area

Special features
- Master bedroom includes dressing area, private bath and walk-in closet
- Secondary bedrooms feature large walk-in closets
- Large living room enjoys access to the rear patio
- U-shaped kitchen features pantry, outdoor access and convenient laundry closet
- 2" x 6" exterior walls available, please order plan #M01-001D-0123
- 3 bedrooms, 2 baths
- Crawl space foundation, drawings also include basement and slab foundations

Price Code B

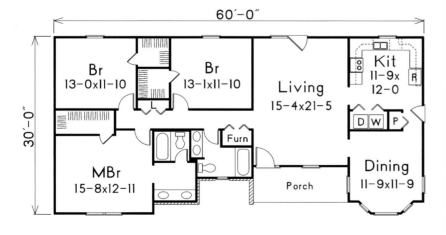

60'-0"

30'-0"

Br
13-0x11-10

Br
13-1x11-10

Living
15-4x21-5

Kit
11-9x
12-0

R

D W P

MBr
15-8x12-11

Furn

Porch

Dining
11-9x11-9

MENARDS

Oakmont

Affordable Atrium Ranch

2,334 total square feet of living area

Special features

◆ Roomy front porch gives home a country flavor

◆ Vaulted great room boasts a fireplace, TV alcove, pass-through snack bar to kitchen and atrium featuring bayed window wall and an ascending stair to family room

◆ Oversized master bedroom features a vaulted ceiling, double-door entry and large walk-in closet

◆ 3 bedrooms, 2 baths, 2-car garage

◆ Walk-out basement foundation

Price Code D

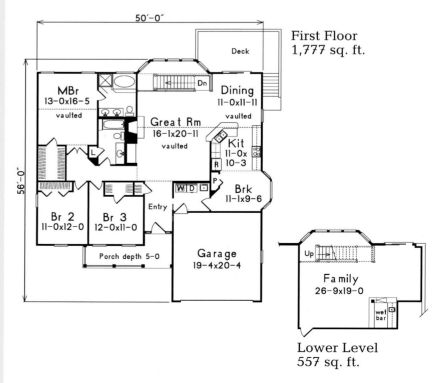

Rear View

First Floor
1,777 sq. ft.

Deck

MBr
13-0x16-5
vaulted

Dining
11-0x11-11
vaulted

Great Rm
16-1x20-11
vaulted

Kit
11-0x
10-3

Brk
11-1x9-6

Br 2
11-0x12-0

Br 3
12-0x11-0

Entry

Garage
19-4x20-4

Porch depth 5-0

50'-0"

56'-0"

Dn

WD

L

R

P

Up

Family
26-9x19-0

wet bar

Lower Level
557 sq. ft.

To order this plan, visit the Menards Building Materials Desk.

Sequoia I

Elegant Double-Door Entry

2,137 total square feet of living area

Special features
◆ Stone and a clerestory window decorate the exterior of this ranch home
◆ Master bedroom features large double walk-in closets, dressing area and private bath
◆ U-shaped kitchen has a breakfast bar and adjacent breakfast nook
◆ Extra large laundry room
◆ 3 bedrooms, 2 baths, 2-car side entry garage
◆ Crawl space foundation, drawings also include basement and slab foundations

Price Code C

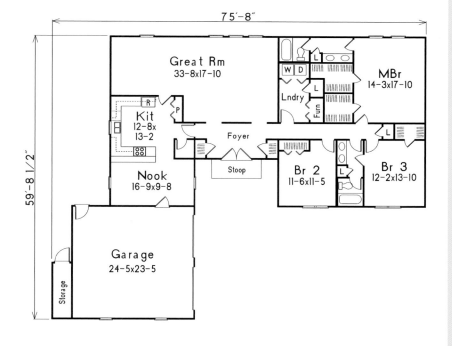

MENARDS

Litchfield

Covered Porch Enhances Exterior

1,428 total square feet of living area

Special features

◆ Garage entrance conveniently leads to the laundry room and kitchen
◆ The kitchen/breakfast area includes a large pantry and plenty of counterspace
◆ Bedrooms are all generously sized and are separated from main living areas for privacy
◆ 3 bedrooms, 2 baths, 3-car side entry garage
◆ Basement foundation

Price Code A

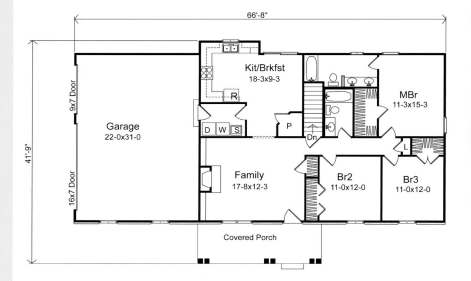

To order this plan, visit the Menards Building Materials Desk.

Sequoia II

Huge Great Room Ideal For Entertaining

2,137 total square feet of living area

Special features

- ◆ Elegant double-door entry with large foyer and double coat closets opens into the grand-size great room
- ◆ All bedrooms enjoy an abundance of closet space and are situated together for easy family living
- ◆ The efficient kitchen enjoys a pantry, storage closet, and adjacent breakfast nook
- ◆ 2" x 6" exterior walls available, please order plan #M01-001D-0129
- ◆ 3 bedrooms, 2 baths, 2-car side entry garage
- ◆ Crawl space foundation, drawings also include basement and slab foundations

Price Code C

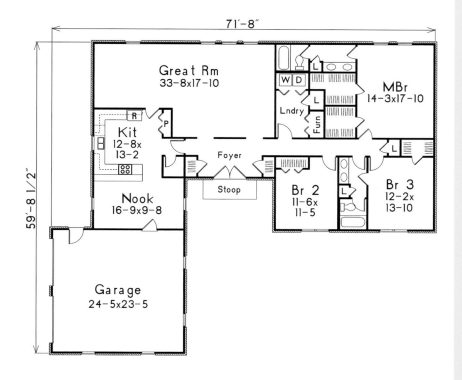

Great Rm
33-8x17-10

Kit
12-8x
13-2

Nook
16-9x9-8

Garage
24-5x23-5

MBr
14-3x17-10

Lndry

Foyer

Stoop

Br 2
11-6x
11-5

Br 3
12-2x
13-10

71'-8"

59'-8 1/2"

Willowhill

Inviting Ranch

1,599 total square feet of living area

Special features

◆ Spacious entry leads to the great room featuring a vaulted ceiling, fireplace and an octagon-shaped dining area with views to the covered patio

◆ The kitchen enjoys a snack counter open to the dining area, a breakfast area with bay window and a built-in pantry

◆ Master bedroom has a sitting area, large walk-in closet and a luxury bath

◆ The laundry room has a convenient half bath and access to the garage with storage area

◆ 4 bedrooms, 2 1/2 baths, 2-car garage

◆ Basement foundation

Price Code B

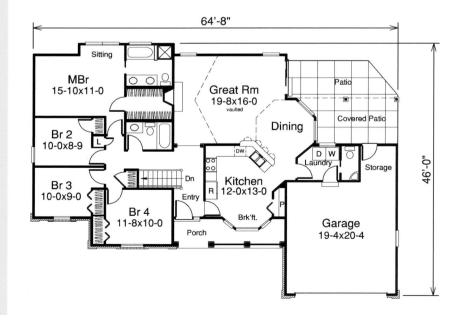

To order this plan, visit the Menards Building Materials Desk.

Plan #M01-008D-0167

Foxcreek

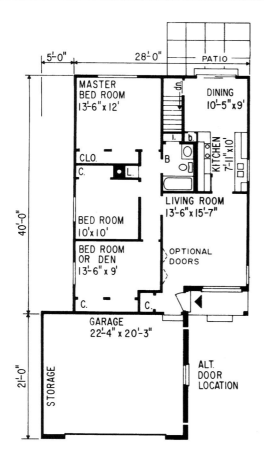

Desirable Design For A Narrow Site

1,082 total square feet of living area

Special features
◆ A convenient coat closet is located just inside the entryway
◆ The large living room offers an optional double-door entry into the den
◆ Extremely functional kitchen leads to the dining room with sliding glass doors opening onto the rear patio
◆ Nice-sized bedrooms enjoy plenty of large closetspace
◆ 3 bedrooms, 1 bath, 2-car garage
◆ Basement or crawl space foundation, please specify when ordering

Price Code AA

To order this plan, visit the Menards Building Materials Desk.

Manor Grove

A Design For Privacy And Flexibility

1,914 total square feet of living area

Special features

◆ Great room features a vaulted ceiling, dining area, entry foyer, corner fireplace and 9' wide sliding doors to rear patio
◆ The secluded secondary bedrooms offer walk-in closets and share a Jack and Jill bath
◆ A multi-purpose room has a laundry alcove and can easily be used as a hobby room, sewing room or small office
◆ Bedroom #4 can be open to the master bedroom suite and utilized as a private study or nursery
◆ 4 bedrooms, 3 baths, 2-car garage
◆ Basement foundation

Price Code C

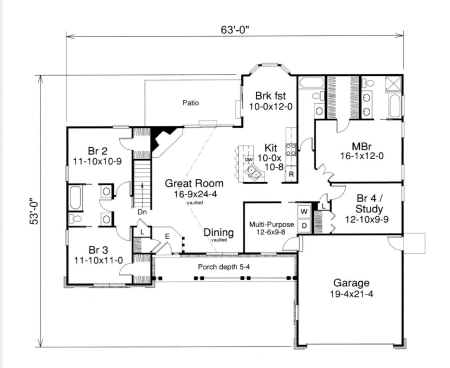

To order this plan, visit the Menards Building Materials Desk.

Spencer

Twin Dormers Accent This Ranch

1,635 total square feet of living area

Special features
◆ This country-style ranch is sure to please with an open living area and private bedrooms
◆ The great room enjoys the openness to the kitchen, a grand fireplace and access to the backyard
◆ A walk-in closet, deluxe bath with whirlpool tub and a vaulted ceiling creates a luxurious master bedroom suite
◆ 3 bedrooms, 2 1/2 baths, 2-car garage
◆ Basement foundation

Price Code AA

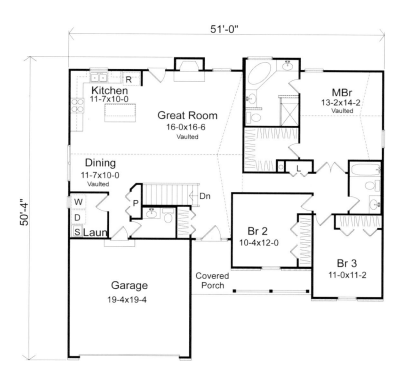

To order this plan, visit the Menards Building Materials Desk.

Westview

Exciting Atrium

2,070 total square feet of living area

Special features

◆ Great room enjoys a fireplace, wet bar and rear views through two-story vaulted atrium
◆ The U-shaped kitchen opens to the breakfast area and features a walk-in pantry, computer center and atrium overlook
◆ Master bath has a Roman whirlpool tub, TV alcove, separate shower/toilet area and linen closet
◆ Extra storage in garage
◆ Atrium opens to 1,062 square feet of optional living area below
◆ 3 bedrooms, 2 baths, 2-car drive-under rear entry garage with storage area
◆ Walk-out basement foundation

Price Code C

Rear View

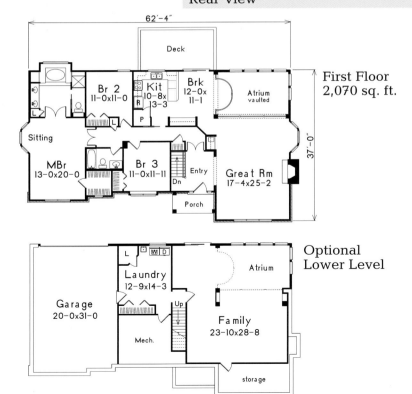

First Floor
2,070 sq. ft.

Optional
Lower Level

To order this plan, visit the Menards Building Materials Desk.

Cherry Manor

Perfectly Suitable For Shallow Lot

1,092 total square feet of living area

Special features

- ◆ Large living room is open to a U-shaped kitchen/dining area which accesses the rear patio through double sliding doors
- ◆ Master bedroom has two large closets which lead to a private bath
- ◆ The two-car garage has ample storage space and also accesses the rear patio
- ◆ 2 bedrooms, 2 baths, 2-car garage
- ◆ Basement, crawl space or slab foundation, please specify when ordering

Price Code AA

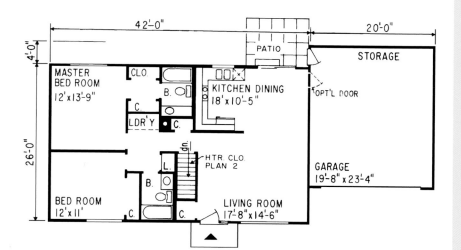

Dartmouth

Prominent Central Living Room Adds Luxurious Focus

2,177 total square feet of living area

Special features

◆ Master bedroom features a sitting area and double-door entry to an elegant master bath
◆ Secondary bedrooms are spacious with walk-in closets and a shared bath
◆ Breakfast room has full windows and opens to the rear porch
◆ Exterior window treatments create a unique style
◆ Kitchen features an island cooktop, eating bar and wet bar that is accessible to the living room
◆ 3 bedrooms, 2 baths, 2-car garage
◆ Slab foundation, drawings also include basement and crawl space foundations

Price Code C

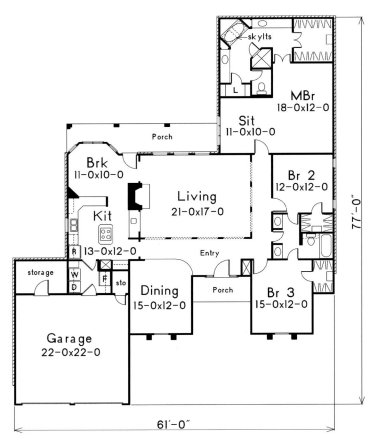

To order this plan, visit the Menards Building Materials Desk.

Lauderdale

Divided Bedroom Areas Lend Privacy

1,833 total square feet of living area

Special features
- Master bedroom suite comes with a garden tub, walk-in closet and bay window
- Walk-through kitchen and breakfast room
- Front bay windows offer a deluxe touch
- Foyer with convenient coat closet opens into large vaulted living room with an attractive fireplace
- 3 bedrooms, 2 baths, 2-car drive under garage
- Basement foundation

Price Code C

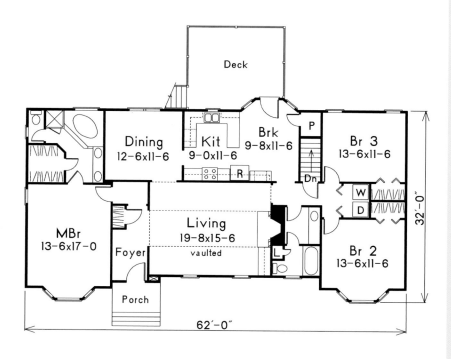

Deck

Dining
12-6x11-6

Kit
9-0x11-6

Brk
9-8x11-6

P

Br 3
13-6x11-6

Dn

R

W
D

MBr
13-6x17-0

Foyer

Living
19-8x15-6
vaulted

Br 2
13-6x11-6

Porch

32'-0"

62'-0"

To order this plan, visit the Menards Building Materials Desk.

MENARDS

Brayden Manor

Perfect Home For A Large Family On A Budget

1,941 total square feet of living area

Special features

- ◆ Interesting roof lines and a spacious front porch with flanking stonework help to fashion this beautiful country home
- ◆ The vaulted great room has a separate entry and bayed dining area suitable for a large family and friends
- ◆ The master bedroom enjoys a big walk-in closet and a gracious bath
- ◆ Four additional bedrooms complete the home, one of which is ideal for a study off the great room
- ◆ 5 bedrooms, 3 baths, 2-car side entry drive under garage
- ◆ Walk-out basement foundation

Price Code C

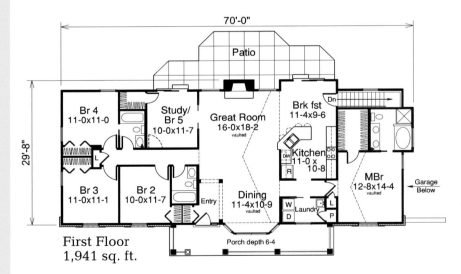

First Floor
1,941 sq. ft.

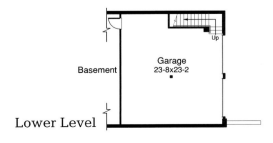

Lower Level

To order this plan, visit the Menards Building Materials Desk.

Sutton

Vaulted Ceiling Adds Spaciousness

990 total square feet of living area

Special features

◆ Wrap-around porch creates a relaxing retreat
◆ Combined family and dining rooms boast a vaulted ceiling
◆ Space for an efficiency washer and dryer unit offers convenience
◆ 2" x 6" exterior walls available, please order plan #M01-058D-0086
◆ 2 bedrooms, 1 bath
◆ Crawl space foundation

Price Code AA

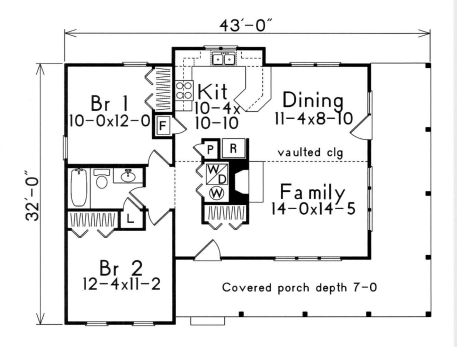

Floor plan labels:
43'-0"
32'-0"
Br 1 — 10-0x12-0
Kit — 10-4x 10-10
Dining — 11-4x8-10
vaulted clg
Family — 14-0x14-5
Br 2 — 12-4x11-2
Covered porch depth 7-0

Foxmyer

Affordable Simplicity

1,310 total square feet of living area

Special features

◆ The combination of brick quoins, roof dormers and an elegant porch creates a classic look

◆ Open-space floor plan has vaulted kitchen, living and dining rooms

◆ The master bedroom is vaulted and enjoys privacy from other bedrooms

◆ A spacious laundry room is convenient to the kitchen and master bedroom with access to an oversized garage

◆ 3 bedrooms, 2 baths, 2-car garage

◆ Basement foundation, drawings also include crawl space and slab foundations

Price Code A

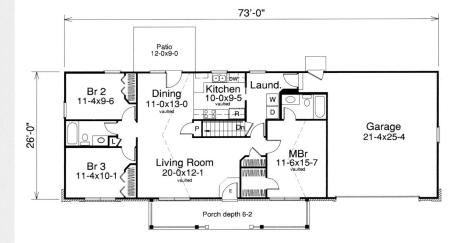

To order this plan, visit the Menards Building Materials Desk.

Greenridge

Convenient Ranch

1,120 total square feet of living area

Special features

◆ Master bedroom includes a half bath with laundry area, linen closet and kitchen access

◆ Kitchen has charming double-door entry, breakfast bar and a convenient walk-in pantry

◆ Welcoming front porch opens to a large living room with coat closet

◆ 3 bedrooms, 1 1/2 baths

◆ Crawl space foundation, drawings also include basement and slab foundations

Price Code AA

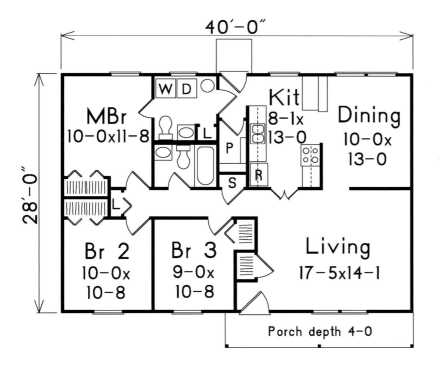

To order this plan, visit the Menards Building Materials Desk.

Brookvale

Spacious Vaulted Living Room

1,789 total square feet of living area

Special features

◆ The relaxing master bedroom features a double-door entry, large walk-in closet and private bath with whirlpool tub

◆ The kitchen enjoys an island with seating area and a pantry

◆ The large laundry area accesses the outdoors on both sides

◆ 3 bedrooms, 2 baths, 2-car side entry garage

◆ Basement foundation

Price Code B

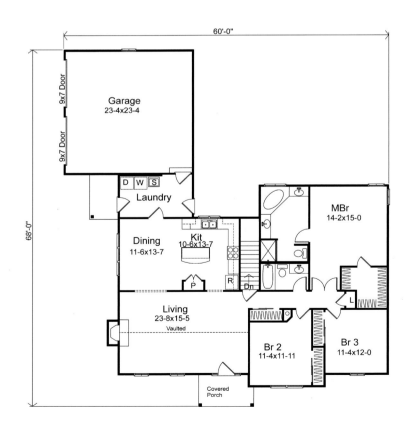

Kasington

Classic Contemporary Wrapped In Brick

2,900 total square feet of living area

Special features
- Energy efficient home with 2" x 6" exterior walls
- The grand-scale great room offers a vaulted ceiling and palladian windows flanking an 8' wide brick fireplace
- A smartly designed built-in-a-bay kitchen features a picture window above sink, huge pantry, cooktop island and is open to a large morning room with 12' of cabinetry
- 1,018 square feet of optional living area on the lower level with family room, walk-in bar and a fifth bedroom with a bath
- 4 bedrooms, 2 1/2 baths, 3-car side entry garage
- Walk-out basement foundation

Price Code E

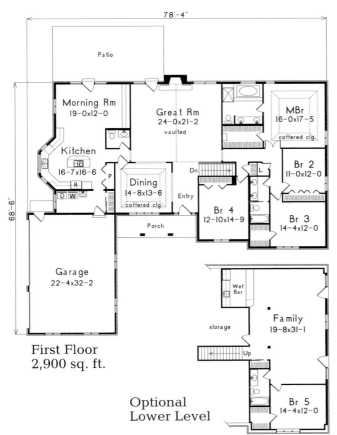

First Floor
2,900 sq. ft.

Optional
Lower Level

Foxridge

Country Ranch With Dramatic Atrium Views

1,533 total square feet of living area

Special features

- ◆ Multiple gables and stonework deliver a warm and inviting exterior
- ◆ The vaulted great room has a fireplace and spectacular views accomplished with a two-story atrium window wall
- ◆ A covered rear porch is easily accessed from the breakfast room or garage
- ◆ The atrium provides an ideal approach to an optional finished walk-out basement
- ◆ 3 bedrooms, 2 baths, 2-car garage
- ◆ Walk-out basement foundation

Price Code B

Rear View

Floor plan:

71'-0"

37'-0"

Atrium vaulted

Dn

MBr 14-8x12-0 vaulted

Great Rm 16-0x17-1 vaulted

Brk fst 11-0x9-6

Covered Deck

Kit 10-9x 11-0

Garage 19-4x21-4

L

Br 2 11-0x9-7

Br 3 12-0x10-0

Entry

Dining 10-4x10-9 vaulted

R

W   D

P

Laundry

Porch depth 5-4

MENARDS

Grandtree

Open Living Areas

1,642 total square feet of living area

Special features

◆ Bedrooms are separated from main living areas for privacy
◆ The vaulted great room is warmed by a grand fireplace
◆ Family activities are sure to be a breeze with this spacious floor plan
◆ A convenient laundry area is located at the garage entrance
◆ 3 bedrooms, 2 baths, 3-car garage
◆ Basement foundation

Price Code B

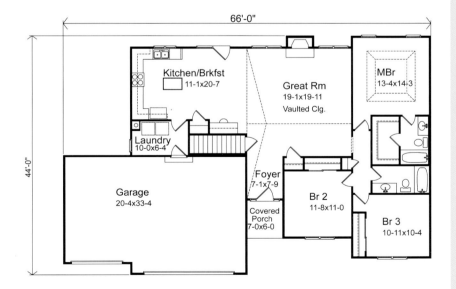

66'-0"

44'-0"

Kitchen/Brkfst
11-1x20-7

Great Rm
19-1x19-11
Vaulted Clg.

MBr
13-4x14-3

Laundry
10-0x6-4

Garage
20-4x33-4

Foyer
7-1x7-9

Covered Porch
7-0x6-0

Br 2
11-8x11-0

Br 3
10-11x10-4

To order this plan, visit the Menards Building Materials Desk.

Henderson

Inviting
Covered Porch

1,670 total square feet of living area

Special features
◆ Enter into this home to find the comforting family room equipped with a fireplace for added warmth
◆ Sliding glass doors highlight the breakfast area and provide access to the rear yard
◆ Pass by the pantry from the garage to the kitchen for easy unloading
◆ 3 bedrooms, 2 baths, 3-car side entry garage
◆ Basement foundation

Price Code AA

To order this plan, visit the Menards Building Materials Desk.

Oakbury

The Plan That Has It All

1,929 total square feet of living area

Special features

- A classic traditional exterior for timeless elegance
- More than a great room for this size home, the grand room features a vaulted ceiling and a brick and wood mantle fireplace flanked by doors to the rear patio
- State-of-the-art U-shaped kitchen has a built-in pantry, computer desk, snack bar and breakfast room with bay window
- The master bedroom includes a vaulted ceiling, large walk-in closet, luxury bath and access to the rear patio
- 4 bedrooms, 3 baths, 3-car side entry garage
- Crawl space foundation, drawings also include slab and basement foundations

Price Code C

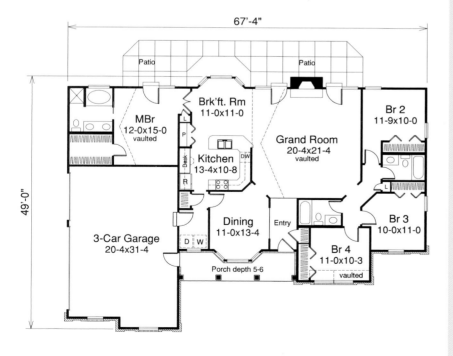

67'-4"

49'-0"

Patio

Patio

MBr
12-0x15-0
vaulted

Brk'ft. Rm
11-0x11-0

Grand Room
20-4x21-4
vaulted

Br 2
11-9x10-0

Kitchen
13-4x10-8

3-Car Garage
20-4x31-4

Dining
11-0x13-4

Entry

Br 3
10-0x11-0

Br 4
11-0x10-3
vaulted

Porch depth 5-6

To order this plan, visit the Menards Building Materials Desk.

221

Briarfield

An Enhancement To Any Neighborhood

1,440 total square feet of living area

Special features

◆ Foyer adjoins massive-sized great room with sloping ceiling and tall masonry fireplace

◆ The kitchen connects to the spacious dining room and features a pass-through to the breakfast bar

◆ Master bedroom enjoys a private bath and two closets

◆ An oversized two-car side entry garage offers plenty of storage for bicycles, lawn equipment, etc.

◆ 3 bedrooms, 2 baths, 2-car side entry garage

◆ Basement foundation, drawings also include crawl space and slab foundations

Price Code A

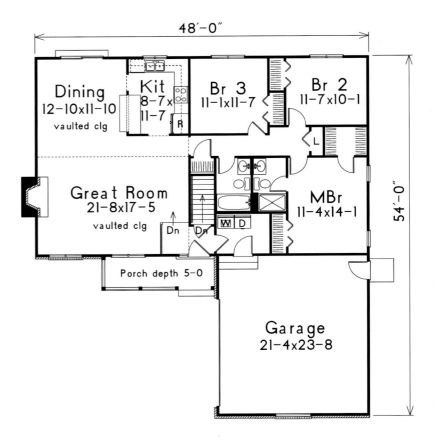

To order this plan, visit the Menards Building Materials Desk.

Westgate

Grand-Sized Living

3,366 total square feet of living area

Special features
◆ Wonderful covered patio is located off the secluded study and breakfast area
◆ Separate dining area for entertaining
◆ Spacious master bedroom has an enormous private bath with walk-in closet
◆ 4 bedrooms, 3 1/2 baths, 2-car side entry garage
◆ Crawl space foundation, drawings also include slab foundation

Price Code F

Floor plan labels:

70'-10"

80'-5"

- Study 16-0x16-0
- Covered Patio
- MBr 21-5x16-0 tray clg
- Brk 14-3x17-6
- Living 20-0x20-5
- Br 4 13-8x15-8
- Br 2 15-5x13-8
- Kitchen 14-3x17-6
- P
- W D
- Dining 13-0x15-0 tray clg
- Foyer
- R
- Br 3 15-5x13-7
- Covered Entry
- Covered Entry
- Garage 22-1x26-2

To order this plan, visit the Menards Building Materials Desk.